D0511262

COOL JOKES

Marks and Spencer p.l.c.
Baker Street, London W1U 8EP
www.marksandspencer.com

This edition © Exclusive Editions 2002

This book was created by Magpie Books,
an imprint of Constable & Robinson Ltd

Cover design and inside illustrations courtesy of Mike Phillips

All rights reserved. This book is sold subject to the
condition that it shall not, by way of trade or
otherwise, be lent, re-sold, hired out or otherwise
circulated in any form of binding or cover other
than that in which it is published and without a
similar condition including this condition being
imposed on the subsequent purchaser.

A copy of the British Library Cataloguing-in-Publication
Data is available from the British Library

Printed in China

ISBN 1-84273-803-8

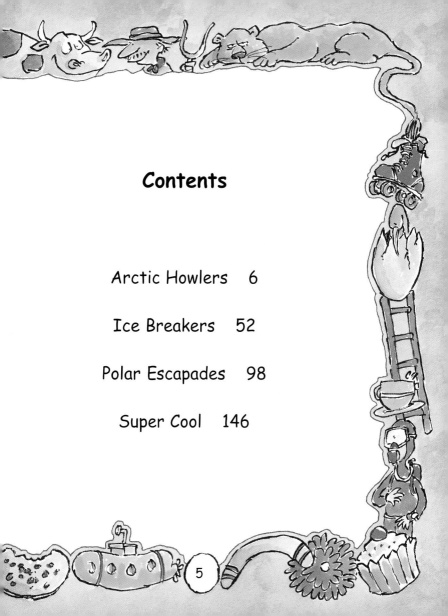

Contents

ARCTIC HOWLERS

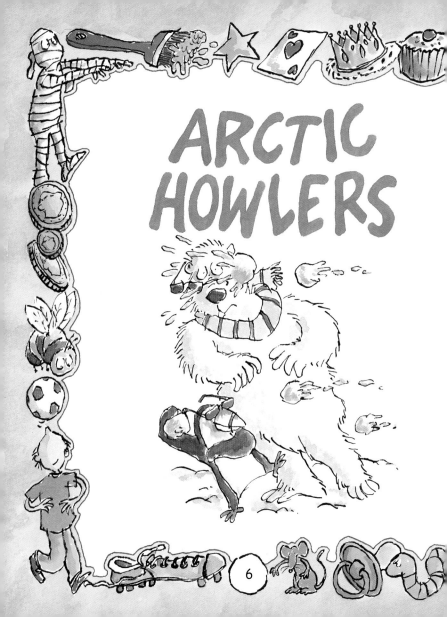

What is a woolly mammoth's favourite sport?
Squash.

What's huge and hairy and goes up and down?
A woolly mammoth in a lift.

Why do woolly mammoths lie on their backs with their legs in the air?
To trip up birds.

How do you make a waterfall?
Throw a bucket of water out of the window.

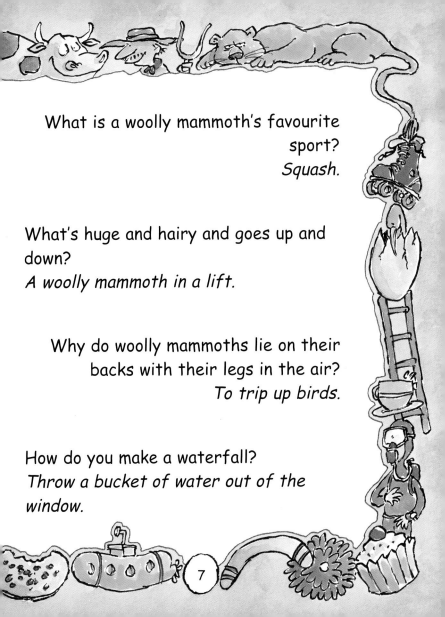

What do you get when a woolly mammoth sky dives?
A large hole.

How do you know when there's a blue whale in your cupboard?
You can't shut the door.

What looks exactly like a woolly mammoth, but weighs nothing?
A woolly mammoth's shadow.

Why did the polar bear eat a clock?
He was just killing time.

What do you get if you cross a woolly mammoth with a kangaroo?
Big holes all over Australia.

Where do woolly mammoths like to go on holiday?
Tusk-any.

How can you tell if there's a woolly mammoth under your bed?
Your nose is touching the ceiling.

What did the wall say to the other wall?
"See you at the corner".

Why did the woolly mammoth eat the stupid man?
Because someone said he was nuts.

How do you get down from a woolly mammoth?
You don't get down from woolly mammoths; you get down from ducks.

How many polar bears can dance on the head of a pin?
None, polar bears can't dance.

Why did the bee fly with his legs crossed?
To get to the BP station.

Why can't woolly mammoths ride bicycles?
Because they don't have thumbs to ring the bell.

Why was the woolly mammoth red?
You would be too if you had so many jokes told about you.

Why do woolly mammoths paint their toenails?
So they can hide in packets of jelly beans.

What did the cavemen do when they saw a woolly mammoth running down the path?
They ran.

What kind of eggs does an evil chicken lay?
Devilled.

What did the cavemen do when they saw a woolly mammoth with sunglasses on running down the path?
Nothing, they didn't recognize him.

Why did the owl 'owl?
Because the woodpecker would peck'er.

What do a grape and a polar bear have in common?
They're both purple, except for the polar bear.

What do you do when your chair breaks?
Call a chairman.

How do you fit a woolly mammoth into a matchbox?
Take out the matches first.

How do you fit a sabre-toothed tiger into a matchbox?
Take out the woolly mammoth.

Why don't woolly mammoths like to go swimming?
Because it's hard to keep their trunks up.

What game do fish like playing the most?
Name that tuna.

How do you make a woolly mammoth float?
Add a woolly mammoth to two scoops of vanilla ice cream and some milk.

What do you get if you cross a jaguar with a woolly mammoth?
A car with a big trunk.

Why did the Abominable Snowman paint his feet yellow?
So he could hide upside down in the custard.

What kind of person has the loudest voice?
The ice-cream man.

What is huge, hairy and has sixteen wheels?
A woolly mammoth on roller skates.

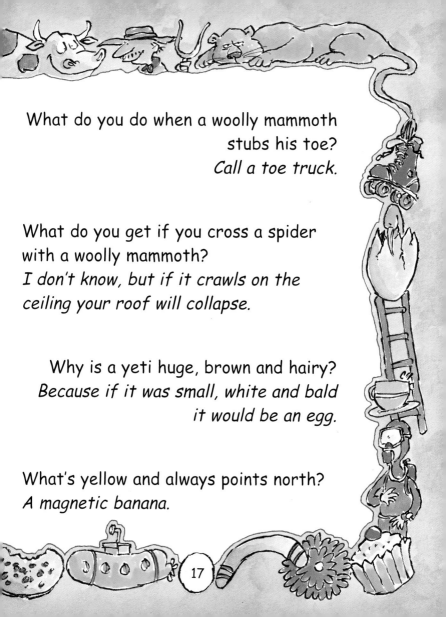

What do you do when a woolly mammoth
stubs his toe?
Call a toe truck.

What do you get if you cross a spider
with a woolly mammoth?
*I don't know, but if it crawls on the
ceiling your roof will collapse.*

Why is a yeti huge, brown and hairy?
*Because if it was small, white and bald
it would be an egg.*

What's yellow and always points north?
A magnetic banana.

Why did the reindeer paint his toenails red?
So he could hide in the cherry tree.

Why is a snail stronger than a woolly mammoth?
A snail carries its house, but a woolly mammoth only carries a trunk.

What happened to Ray when a woolly mammoth stepped on him?
He became an X-Ray.

Who sleeps at the bottom of the sea?
Jack the kipper.

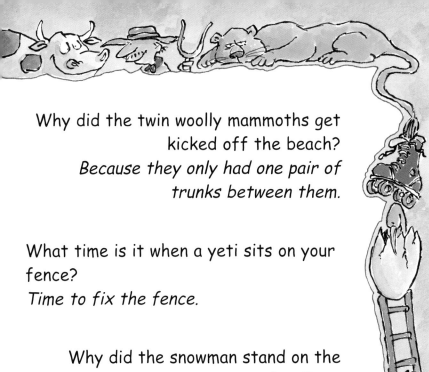

Why did the twin woolly mammoths get kicked off the beach?
Because they only had one pair of trunks between them.

What time is it when a yeti sits on your fence?
Time to fix the fence.

Why did the snowman stand on the marshmallow?
So he wouldn't fall in the hot chocolate.

What is a dolphin's favourite TV show?
Whale of fortune.

How do you know if a woolly mammoth has been in your fridge?
There are footprints in the butter.

What's the difference between a post box and a woolly mammoth?
Don't know? I'll never ask you to post a letter.

What do you get if you cross a woolly mammoth with a mouse?
Great big holes in the skirting board.

What game do cows play at parties?
Moosical chairs.

How does a walrus get up a tree?
He sits on an acorn and waits for it to grow.

How does a walrus get out of a tree?
He sits on a leaf and waits for autumn.

What's the difference between woolly mammoths and elephants?
Elephants don't need to carry combs.

Did you hear about the fish that went deaf?
He had to buy a herring aid.

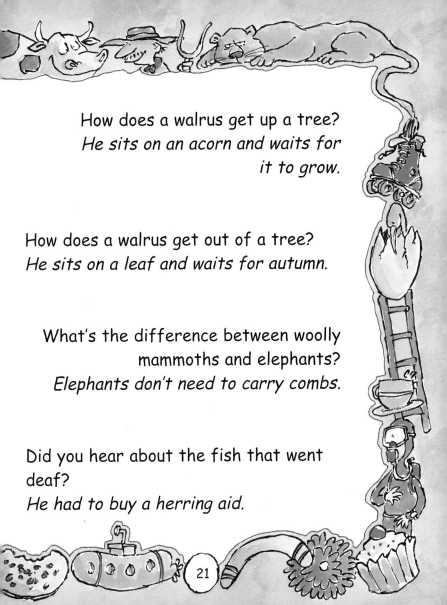

What is the difference between a
penguin and a grape?
Penguins don't have pips.

How do you get a woolly mammoth
into a fridge?
1. Open door.
2. Insert woolly mammoth.
3. Close door.

How do you get a polar bear into a fridge?
1. Open door.
2. Remove woolly mammoth.
3. Insert polar bear.
4. Close door.

How do you get a woolly mammoth out of a fridge?
Tell him it's cooler in the freezer.

How do you get four woolly mammoths into a mini?
Two in the front, two in the back.

What did the fifth woolly mammoth in the mini discover?
The sunroof.

How do you know there are three woolly mammoths in your fridge?
There'll be one waiting outside in the mini.

What is a husky dog's favourite sport?
Formula 1 drooling.

How do you get a woolly mammoth out of the water?
Wet.

How do you get two woolly mammoths out of the water?
One by one.

How do you smuggle a polar bear across the border?
Put a slice of bread on each side, and call him "lunch".

What is a sick reptile?
An illigator.

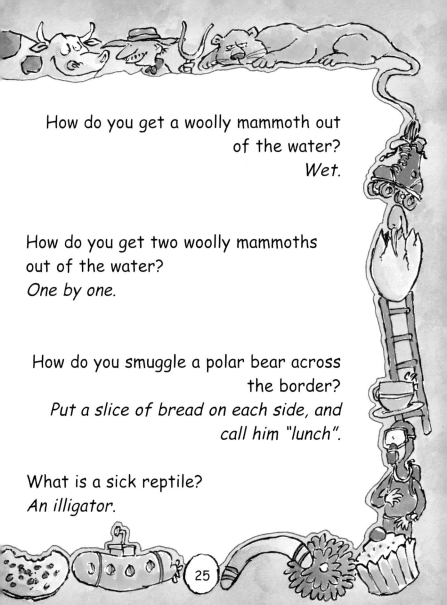

Why are woolly mammoths woolly?
Because silk is too expensive.

Why are woolly mammoths wrinkled?
Because they sit in the bath too long.

Where had the runner been?
To see the celery stalk.

Why did the sea-lion fall out of the tree?
Because it was dead.

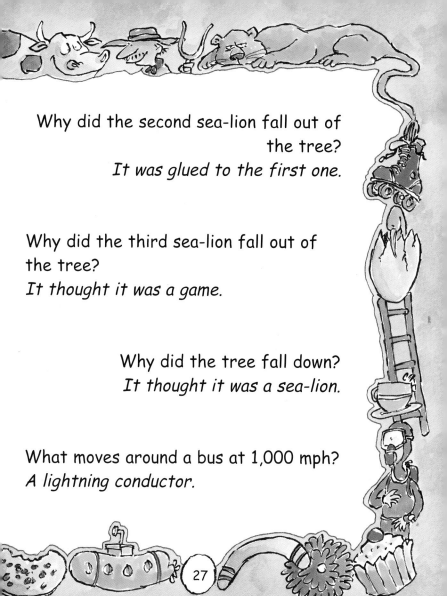

Why did the second sea-lion fall out of the tree?
It was glued to the first one.

Why did the third sea-lion fall out of the tree?
It thought it was a game.

Why did the tree fall down?
It thought it was a sea-lion.

What moves around a bus at 1,000 mph?
A lightning conductor.

Why were there so many woolly mammoths running around in the Stone Age?
Because cavemen didn't have fridges.

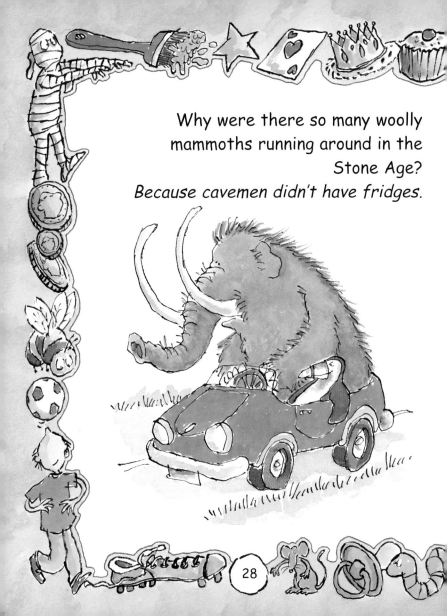

What was the woolly mammoth doing on the motorway?
About five miles per hour.

How do you shoot a blue woolly mammoth?
With a blue woolly mammoth gun, of course.

What do you call two woolly mammoths on a bicycle?
Optimistic.

What do you call a musical insect?
A humbug.

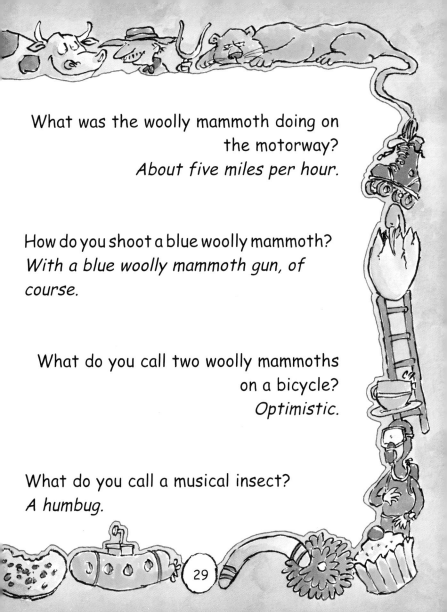

Why are polar bears' feet shaped the
way they are?
To fit on lily pads.

Why isn't it safe to walk on lily pads
between two and four in the afternoon?
*That's when the polar bears are walking
on the lily pads.*

Why are frogs so short?
*They walk on lily pads between two and
four in the afternoon.*

What's green, curly and religious?
Lettuce pray.

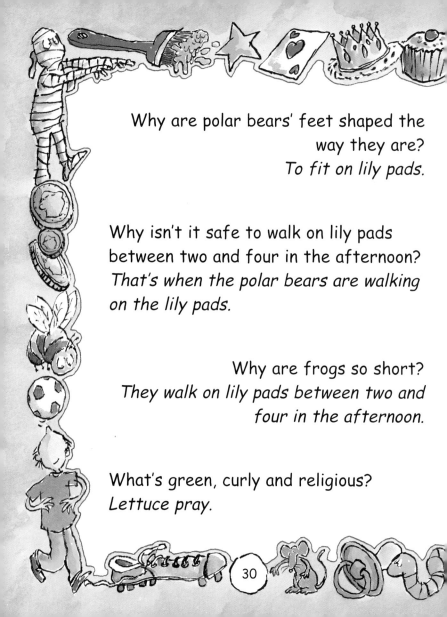

What do you get if you take a woolly mammoth into the city?
Free parking.

Why do ducks have flat feet?
From stamping out forest fires.

Why do yetis have flat feet?
From stamping out flaming ducks.

What is a dog's favourite food?
Anything that's on your plate.

What does it tell you when you see three polar bears walking down the street wearing blue sweatshirts?
They're all on the same team.

How do you know if there's a woolly mammoth in your bed?
All the bed clothes are taken.

Why do woolly mammoths have trunks?
Because they would look silly with glove compartments.

How do fish go into business?
They start on a small scale.

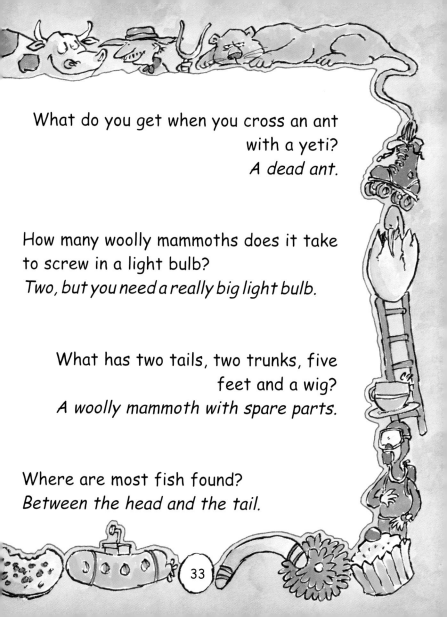

What do you get when you cross an ant with a yeti?
A dead ant.

How many woolly mammoths does it take to screw in a light bulb?
Two, but you need a really big light bulb.

What has two tails, two trunks, five feet and a wig?
A woolly mammoth with spare parts.

Where are most fish found?
Between the head and the tail.

What is more difficult than getting a woolly mammoth into the back seat of your car?
Getting two woolly mammoths into the back seat of your car.

What do you call a fly with no wings?
A walk.

How do you catch a squirrel?
Climb into a tree and act like a nut.

Why didn't the penguin do well at school?
All his marks were below "c" level.

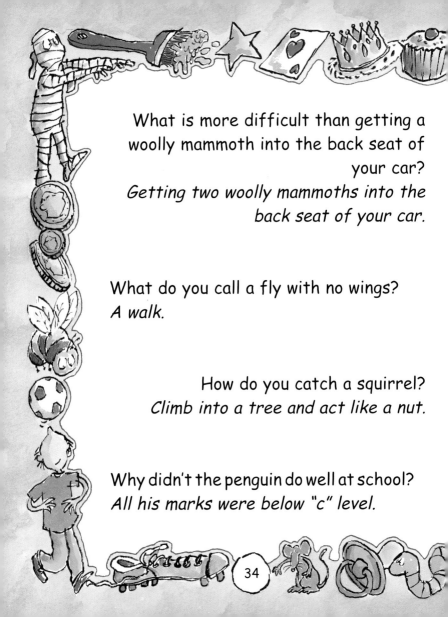

How many woolly mammoths can you fit into a hatchback?
Five — two in the front, two in the back, and one in the glove compartment.

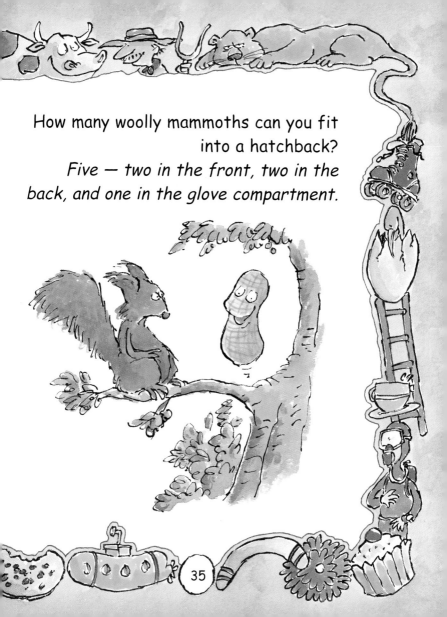

Why don't cannibals eat comedians?
Because they taste funny.

How do you describe the average cannibal?
A guy with a wife and ate children.

What do you call a missing parrot?
A polygon.

How long does it take to learn to skate?
About a dozen sittings.

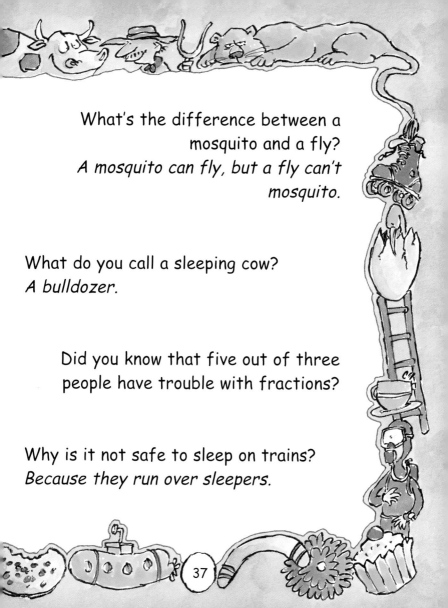

What's the difference between a
mosquito and a fly?
*A mosquito can fly, but a fly can't
mosquito.*

What do you call a sleeping cow?
A bulldozer.

Did you know that five out of three
people have trouble with fractions?

Why is it not safe to sleep on trains?
Because they run over sleepers.

Did you hear about the cat that swallowed a ball of yarn?
She had mittens.

Why can't skeletons play music in church?
They have no organs.

What did the bald man say when he got a comb for his birthday?
"Thanks, I'll never part with it."

Why did the clock get angry?
It was wound up.

What do you call a parrot wearing a raincoat?
Polly unsaturated.

What did the grapes say when the monks stepped on them?
Nothing — they just let out a little whine.

When is a car not a car?
When it turns into a driveway.

To whom do fish go to borrow money?
The loan shark.

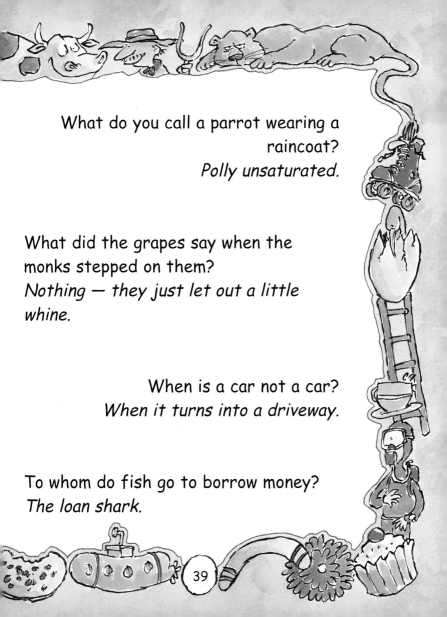

Which insects can tell the time?
Clockroaches.

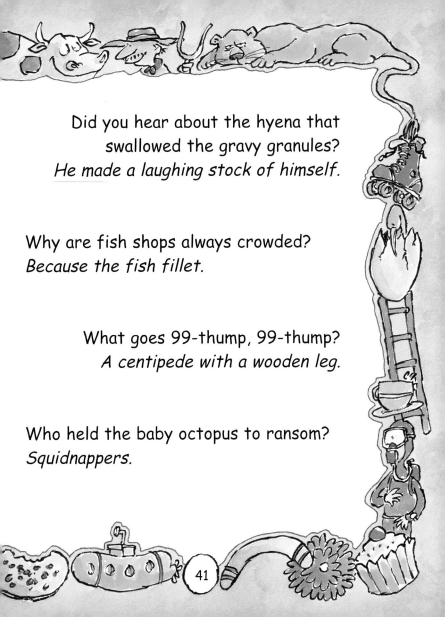

Did you hear about the hyena that
swallowed the gravy granules?
He made a laughing stock of himself.

Why are fish shops always crowded?
Because the fish fillet.

What goes 99-thump, 99-thump?
A centipede with a wooden leg.

Who held the baby octopus to ransom?
Squidnappers.

What bird can lift the most weight?
A crane.

What's long, yellow and surprisingly crisp?
An apple in disguise.

What's bright yellow and can't swim?
A bulldozer.

What fish do road-menders use?
Pneumatic krill.

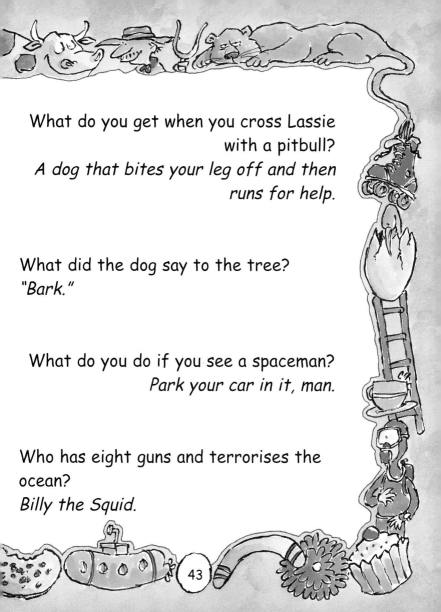

What do you get when you cross Lassie with a pitbull?
A dog that bites your leg off and then runs for help.

What did the dog say to the tree?
"Bark."

What do you do if you see a spaceman?
Park your car in it, man.

Who has eight guns and terrorises the ocean?
Billy the Squid.

What do you call spending the afternoon with a cranky rabbit?
A bad hare day.

What do you get when you drop a piano down a mineshaft?
A-flat minor.

What did one casket say to the other casket?
"Is that you coffin?"

What happened to the cold jellyfish?
It set.

What's the best time to go to the dentist?
Tooth hurty.

If athletes get athlete's foot what do astronauts get?
Mistle toe.

What did the cannibal do when he saw an "All you can eat restaurant"?
He ate all the customers.

What's the coldest creature in the sea?
A blue whale.

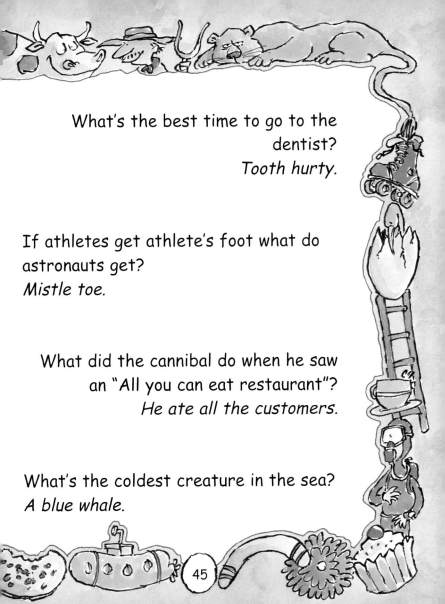

Did you hear about the cannibal who came home late for dinner?
His wife gave him an evil eye.

There are three kinds of people in the world.
Those who can count, and those who can't.

What do you call a boomerang that doesn't work?
A stick.

How did the Vikings send secret messages?
By norse code.

What do you get when you put a canary in a blender?
Shredded tweet.

Why do woolly mammoths wear sandals?
So that they don't sink into the sand.

What do you get if you cross a woolly mammoth with a whale?
A submarine with a built-in snorkel.

Who invented fractions?
Henry the 1/8th.

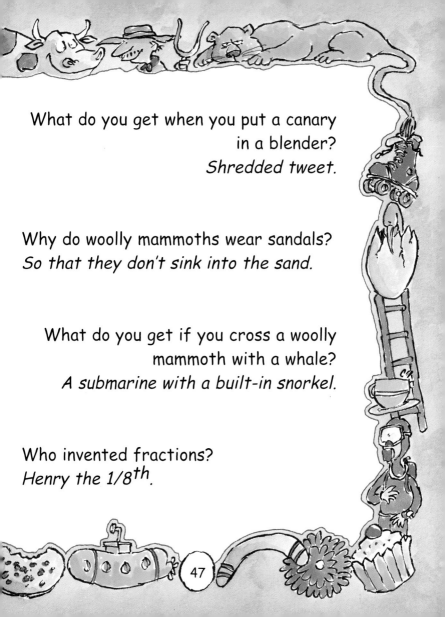

Why do seagulls fly over the sea?
If they flew over the bay then they would be bagels.

What did one frog say to the other?
Time's sure fun when you're having flies.

How do you catch a rabbit?
Hide behind a tree and make carrot noises.

What kind of money do fishermen make?
Net profits.

How do you organize a space party?
You planet.

What do you get when you cross a
hundred pigs with a hundred deer?
Two hundred sows and bucks.

Why don't anteaters get sick?
Because they're full of anty-bodies.

Where does seaweed look for a job?
In the kelp-wanted ads.

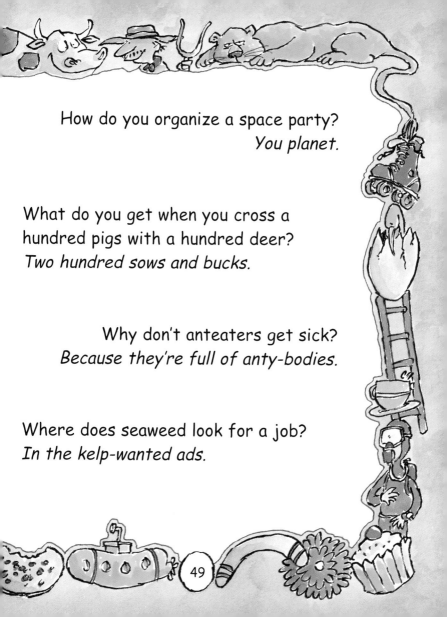

How do you know if there is an Abominable Snowman in the sweet shop?
Its bike is outside.

How do you know if there are two Abominable Snowmen in the sweet shop?
There's a dent in the crossbar.

How do you know if there are three Abominable Snowmen in the sweet shop?
Stand on the bike and have a look in the window.

Where do fish wash?
In a river basin.

What did the mayonnaise say to the fridge?
"Would you mind closing the door, I'm dressing."

When is a door not a door?
When it's ajar.

Why do you have to go to bed?
Because the bed won't come to you.

Why is music like an icy pavement?
You could B flat if you don't C sharp.

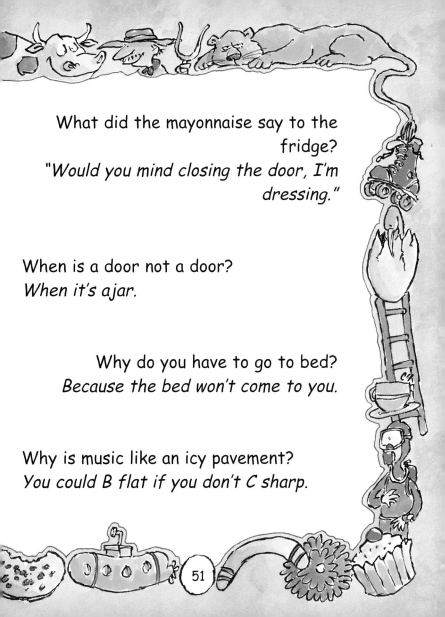

ICE BREAKERS

What did the sea say to the iceberg?
Nothing, it just waved.

What's grey, eats fish and lives in
Washington DC?
The presidential seal.

Where do penguins go to dance?
The snow ball.

What creature can fly underwater?
A fly in a submarine.

Why did the penguin cross the road?
To go with the floe.

54

What do penguins take to school?
Ice-pack lunch.

Why don't penguins carry fish in their pockets?
Because they don't have pockets.

Why do penguins carry fish in their beaks?
I told you — because they don't have pockets.

Who has large antlers and wears white gloves?
Mickey Moose.

Why are penguins popular on the Internet?
Because they have web feet.

How do penguins drink?
Out of beak-ers.

What's a penguin's favourite salad?
Iceberg lettuce.

When are eyes not eyes?
When a cold wind makes them water.

Who's the penguin's favourite aunt?
Aunt-arctica.

How does a penguin make pancakes?
With his flippers.

Why are penguins good racing drivers?
Because they're always in pole position.

Why did the boy take his nose apart in winter?
He wanted to see what made it run.

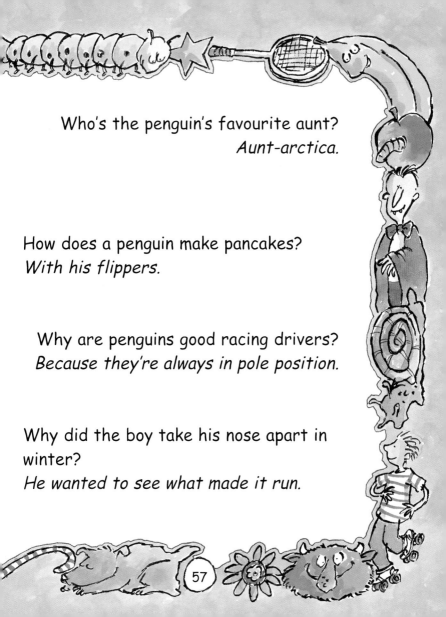

What do little penguins sing when their father brings fish home for dinner?
"Freeze a jolly good fellow."

What do you call a man who floats across an ocean?
Bob.

What do you call a gigantic polar bear?
Nothing, you just run away.

What happens to a reindeer when it stands out in the rain?
It gets wet.

What's black white black white black white black white black white?
A penguin rolling down stairs.

Where do penguins keep their money?
In the snow bank.

What do you get if you cross an elephant
with the Abominable Snowman?
A jumbo yeti.

Why was the pelican kicked out of the
hotel?
Because he had a big bill.

Where does money fall like snow?
*Wherever there's a change in the
weather.*

What do you get if you cross a yeti
with a kangaroo?
A fur coat with big pockets.

Why don't polar bears buy shoes?
*Because when they wear them they still
have bear feet.*

Could you kill the Abominable Snowman
just by throwing eggs at him?
Of course — he'd be eggs-terminated.

What kind of tree is hairy?
A fur tree.

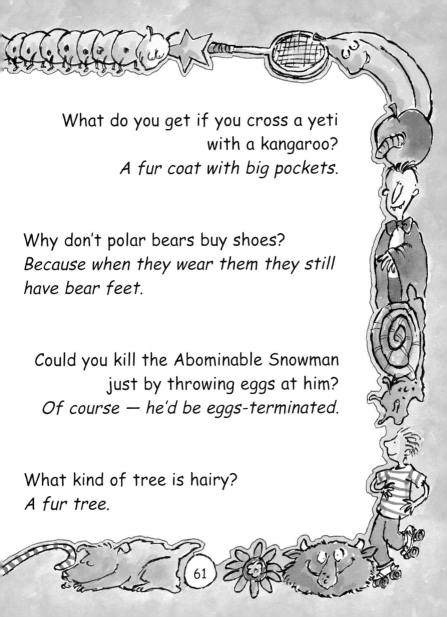

What do you get if you cross the Abominable Snowman with Dracula?
Frostbite.

What do you give a seasick yeti?
Plenty of room.

What's very fat, very ugly and loves fetching sticks?
Jabba the Mutt.

What do you call prehistoric ship disasters?
Tyrannosaurus wrecks.

Can the Abominable Snowman jump very high?
Hardly — he can only just clear his throat.

What do you do if you find a yeti sleeping in your bed?
Sleep somewhere else.

Where are yetis found?
They're so big they're hardly ever lost.

Why was Batman sad in the autumn?
Because Robin flew south for the winter.

Why shouldn't you dance with a yeti?
Because you might get flat feet.

What do you call a yeti in a phone box?
Stuck.

How did the yeti feel when he had flu?
Abominable.

What do yetis eat on top of Everest?
High tea.

What animal talks too much?
A yak.

What kind of man doesn't like to sit in front of the fire?
The Abominable Snowman.

Why was the Abominable Snowman's dog called Frost?
Because Frost bites.

What did the Abominable Snowman do after he had his teeth pulled out?
He ate the dentist.

Why was the bird arrested?
Because he was a robin.

What did one yeti say to the other?
"I'm afraid I just don't believe in people."

What is the Abominable Snowman's favourite book?
War and Frozen Peas.

What do yetis call their offspring?
Chill-dren.

If a girl slips on the ice why can't her brother help her up?
He can't be a brother and assist her too.

Why did the Abominable Snowman send his father to Siberia?
Because he wanted frozen pop.

Did you hear the joke about the fierce yeti?
It'll make you roar.

Why do cows wear bells?
Because their horns don't work.

What did the stag say to her children?
"Hurry up, deers!"

What is a twip?
What a wabbit takes when he wides a twain.

What is grey and has big ears and a trunk?
A mouse going on holiday.

What kind of bears like to go out in the rain?
Drizzly bears.

When is a boat like a pile of snow?
When it's adrift.

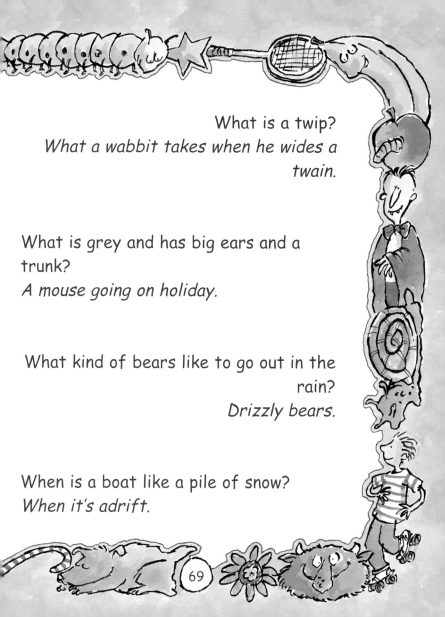

69

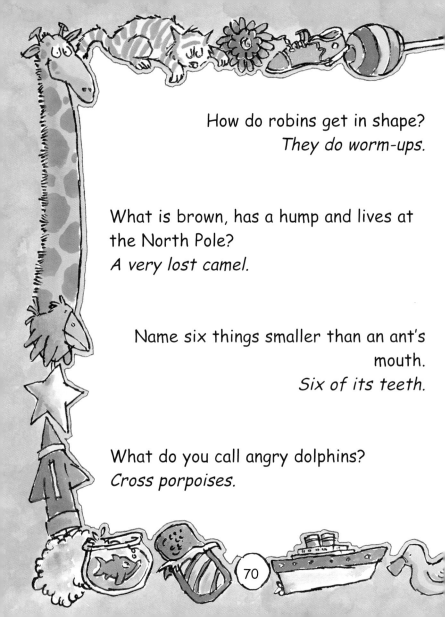

How do robins get in shape?
They do worm-ups.

What is brown, has a hump and lives at the North Pole?
A very lost camel.

Name six things smaller than an ant's mouth.
Six of its teeth.

What do you call angry dolphins?
Cross porpoises.

Where do horses go when they are sick?
To the horsepital.

What did the snowball do when it stopped rolling?
Looked round.

How do you stop a dog barking in the back seat of a car?
Put him in the front seat.

What side of a turkey do the feathers grow on?
The outside.

When is the Arctic Ocean like a piece of string?
When a ship makes knots in it.

What's the difference between a dog
and a painter?
*One sheds his coat, and the other coats
his shed.*

What did the scientist say when he
found bones on the moon?
"The cow didn't make it."

Why can't a leopard hide?
Because he's always spotted.

Where are there no fat people?
In Finland.

What do cows do on Saturday nights?
Go to the moooooovies.

What do nuclear scientists like to eat?
Fission chips.

What kind of dog tells the time?
A watchdog.

What do you use to cut through giant waves?
A sea-saw.

What do you call a cow that has just
had a baby?
Decalfinated.

What do you call a monkey holding a
firecracker?
A baboom.

How do you stop a rhino from charging?
Take away its credit card.

What's big, black, and eats polar bears?
A big, black polar bear-eater.

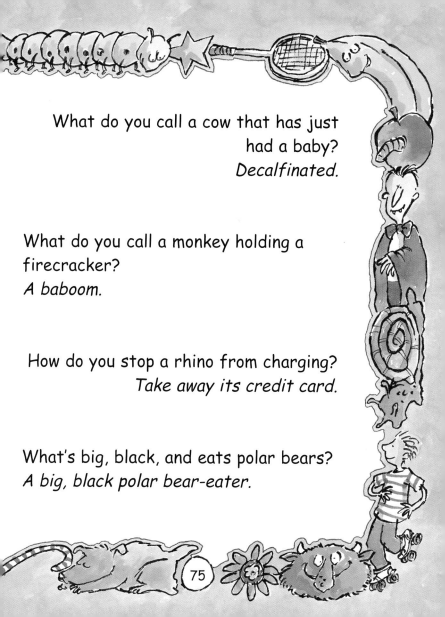

What do you call a box of fifty ducks?
A box of quackers.

What do you call a pony with a sore throat?
A little hoarse.

What mouse doesn't eat cheese?
A computer mouse.

How do rabbits send letters?
By haremail.

When is a painting like a tin of sardines?
When it's done in oils.

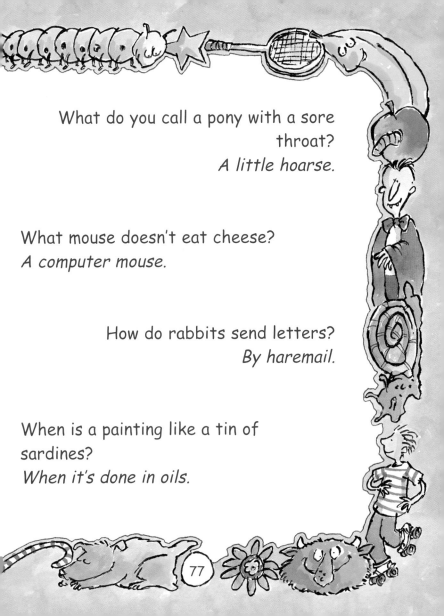

What kind of car does a cat drive?
A Cat-a-lac.

What's the difference between a piano and a fish?
You can tune a piano, but you can't tuna fish.

What do sharks eat with their peanut butter?
Jellyfish.

What kind of tie does a pig wear?
A pig's tie.

What did the boy octopus say to the girl octopus?
I want to hold your hand, hand, hand, hand, hand, hand, hand, hand.

What do you do with a blue whale?
Put him by the fire to warm him up.

How do you communicate with a fish?
Drop it a line.

What fish is good for pudding?
A jellyfish.

Where do sheep go to get haircuts?
To the baa baa's shop.

What do cats eat for breakfast?
Mice Crispies.

What do you get if you cross a duck with a rooster?
A bird that wakes you up at the quack of dawn.

What happens to a penguin before it grows up?
It grows down.

What is a slug?
A snail with a housing problem.

What has a head like a dog, a tail like a dog and paws like a dog but isn't a dog?
A puppy.

How does a dog stop a video recorder?
He presses the paws button.

What part of a fish weighs the most?
The scales.

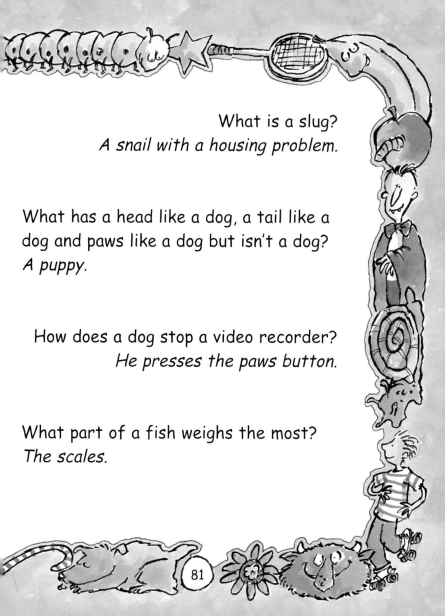

Where do tough chickens come from?
Hard-boiled eggs.

What do you call a camel with no humps?
Humphrey.

What says "quick, quick"?
A duck with hiccups.

How do mountains hear?
They have mountaineers.

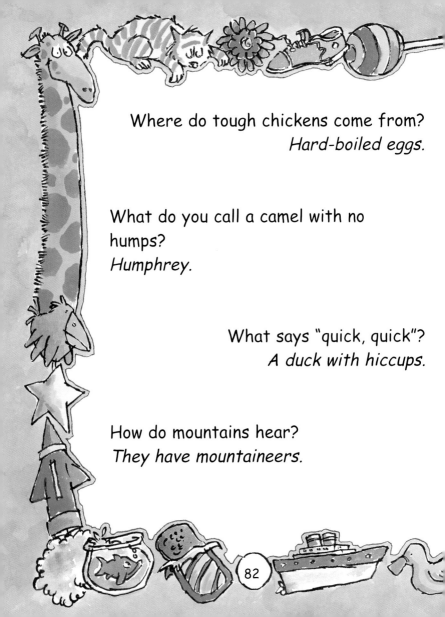

82

What is yellow and very dangerous?
Shark infested custard.

What happens when a tap, a dog and a tomato run a race?
Well, the dog is in the lead, the tap is running and the tomato is trying to catch up.

Why can't Cinderella play football?
Because she always runs away from the ball.

Where do monkeys make toast?
Under a gorilla.

What do you get if you cross a Mars bar with an elk?
A chocolate mousse.

What do you get if you sit under a cow?
A pat on the head.

Why did the chicken cross the playground?
To get to the other slide.

What did one firefly say to the other when his light went out?
"Give me a push, my battery is dead."

What sort of drink would you get from a polar bear?
Iced tea.

Why was Cinderella bad at sports?
Her coach was a pumpkin.

What do footballers drink?
Penaltea.

"Doctor, Doctor! I think I've swallowed a ten pound note."
"Come back tomorrow and we'll see if there's any change."

What kind of coat can you put on when it's wet?
A coat of paint.

Why did the bubble gum cross the road?
Because it was stuck to the chicken's foot.

What do you call a strawberry that's just been run over?
Traffic jam.

Why did the tomato blush?
Because he saw the salad dressing.

Who designed the first rain coat?
Anna Rack.

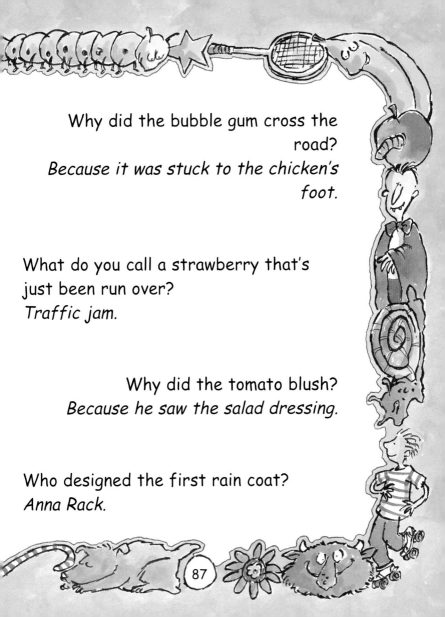

87

How do you get six donkeys in a fire engine?
Two in the front, two in the back and two on the top shouting "Eeyore, eeyore, eeyore".

How do you know which end of a worm is its head?
Tickle it and see which end laughs.

What did one candle say to the other candle?
"Shall we go out tonight?"

What's the fastest cake in the world?
Scone.

On a cold winter's day what are you likely to see close at hand?
A glove.

What do you get when you cross a camera with a crocodile?
A snap shot.

What do you call a man with a car on his head?
Jack.

Why are fish afraid of computers?
Because of the Internet.

How does an octopus go to war?
Fully-armed.

Where did the policeman live?
Nine-nine-nine, Letsbe Avenue.

A man was driving a black car, his lights were off, the moon wasn't out, a woman crossed the road in front of him. How did he see her?
It was the middle of the day.

Why is six afraid of seven?
Because seven, ate, nine.

What do you get if you cross a yak with a parrot?
A yakkety-yak.

Why did the chicken cross the road?
Don't ask me, ask the chicken.

What is red and stupid?
A blood clot.

What's the fastest vegetable?
The runner bean.

What did the finger say to the thumb?
"People will say we're in glove!"

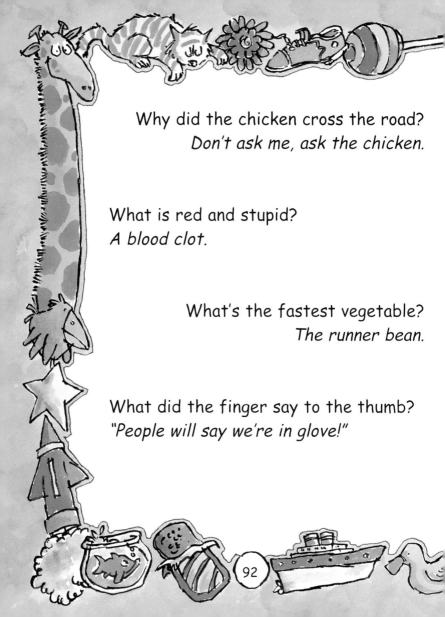

What do you call a boy with a seagull on his head?
Cliff.

Where do spiders play football?
Web-ley.

What has six legs but can't walk?
Three pairs of trousers.

What kind of sea creature is good at adding up?
An octoplus.

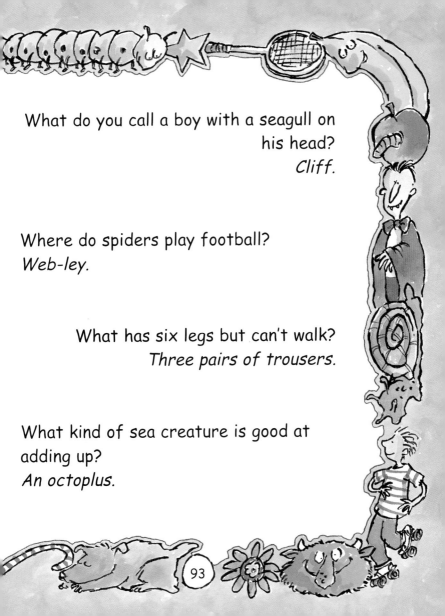

What did the zero say to the eight?
"Nice belt."

What's black and white and read all over?
A newspaper.

What do you get if you cross a cat with a parrot?
A carrot.

What would you do if you broke your leg in two places?
Stay away from those places in future.

What did the traffic light say to the car?
"Don't look now, I'm changing."

Why did the hedgehog cross the road?
To see his flatmate.

How did the idiot burn his ear?
The telephone rang while he was ironing.

What do you call a chicken crossing the road?
Poultry in motion.

What's the definition of "debate"?
It's what lures de fish.

If a butcher is seven feet tall and wears size fifteen shoes, what does he weigh?
Meat.

What did Godzilla say to King Kong when they were having a walk?
"It's a small world".

What is white and goes up?
A confused snowflake.

What happens when a thousand labourers fall off a mountain?
You get a navvy-lanche.

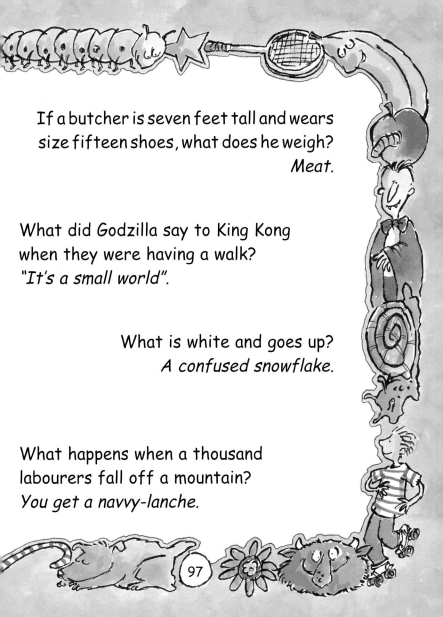

POLAR ESCAPADES

What noise wakes up penguins?
The crack of dawn.

Why did the snowman die with his boots on?
Because he didn't want to stub his toe when he kicked the bucket.

What do you get if you cross a polar bear with a flower?
I don't know, but I'm not going to smell it.

Who is a husky dog's favourite comedian?
Growlcho Marx.

Have you ever seen a man-eating polar bear?

No, but in a café I once saw a man eating chicken.

Why was the seal swimming backstroke?
It had just had lunch and didn't want to swim on a full stomach.

How do you stop a cold getting to your chest?
Tie a knot in your neck.

What lies at the bottom of the Arctic Sea and shivers?
A nervous wreck.

Why didn't the husky dog speak to his foot?
Because it's not polite to talk back to your paw.

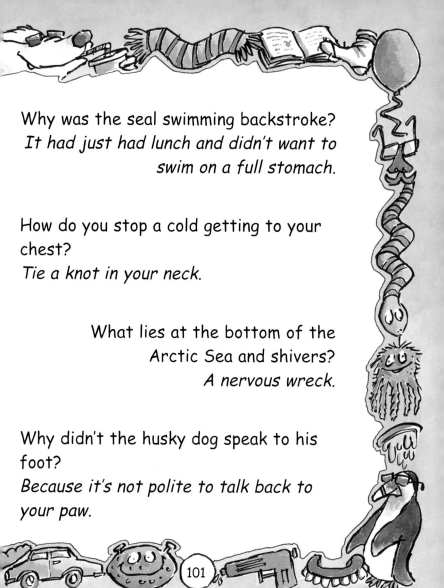

Why did Father Christmas take a pencil
to bed?
To draw the curtains.

What do you call a mammoth wearing
five balaclavas and a big furry hat?
Anything you like — he can't hear you.

Why did the policeman call his dog
Camera?
Because it was always snapping.

What happened when the husky dog
went to the flea circus?
He stole the show.

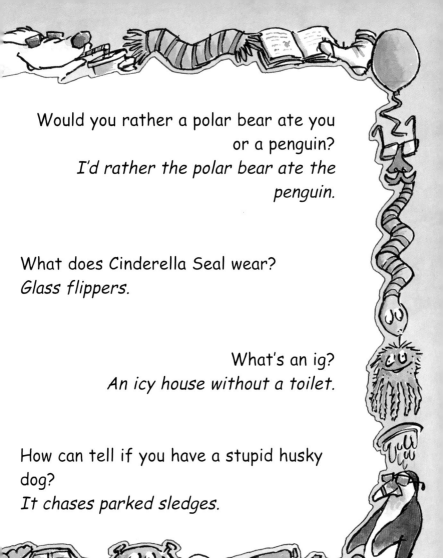

Would you rather a polar bear ate you
or a penguin?
*I'd rather the polar bear ate the
penguin.*

What does Cinderella Seal wear?
Glass flippers.

What's an ig?
An icy house without a toilet.

How can tell if you have a stupid husky
dog?
It chases parked sledges.

103

There's an igloo made of ice,
it has ice chairs, ice floors and
ice walls, an ice door and an ice roof.
What are the stairs made of?
Igloos don't have stairs.

What do you get if you cross a teddy
bear with a pig?
A teddy boar.

What should you call a bald teddy?
Fred bear.

Where are husky dogs trained?
In mush rooms.

What steps would you take if an angry polar bear came rushing towards you?
Great big ones.

What animal do you look like when you get into the bath?
A little bear.

Why is a polar bear cheap to have as a pet?
It lives on ice.

Who ate his animals two by two?
Noah Shark.

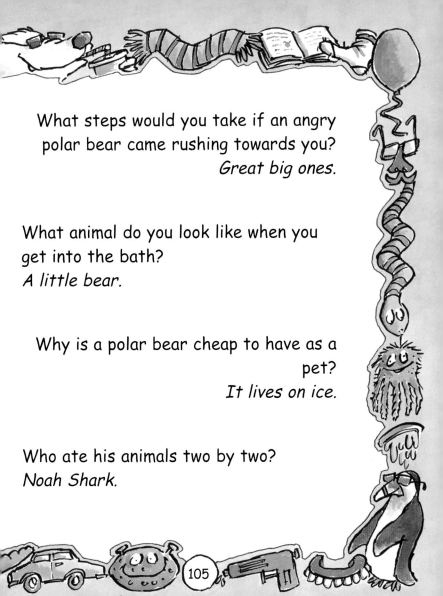

Have you ever hunted bear?
No, but I've been shooting in my shorts.

How do you hire a polar bear?
Put him on stilts.

What's a teddy bear's favourite pasta?
Tagliateddy.

What do you get if you cross a giraffe
with a husky dog?
*An animal that barks at low flying
aircraft.*

Why shouldn't you take polar bears to the zoo?
Because they'd rather go to the cinema.

What kind of money do polar bears use?

Ice lolly.

What do you call a big white bear with a hole in his middle?

A polo bear.

Why do polar bears like bald men?

Because they have a great, white, bear place.

What is the difference between Father Christmas and a warm dog?

Father Christmas wears a whole suit, a dog just pants.

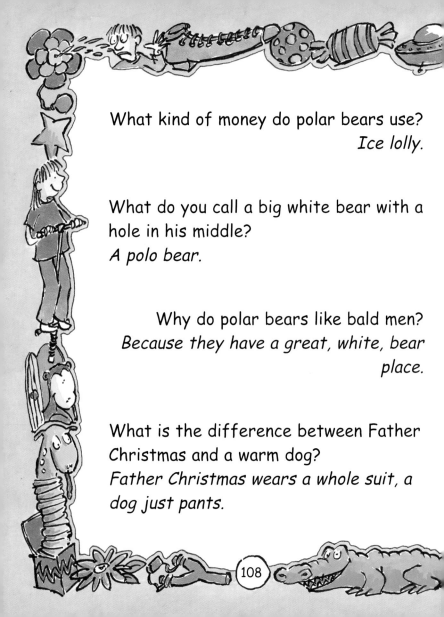

Why was the little bear so spoiled?
Because its mother panda'd to its every whim.

How do you start a teddy bear race?
Ready, teddy, go.

What is huge, white and furry but invisible?
No polar bears.

Why don't husky dogs make good dancers?
They have two left feet.

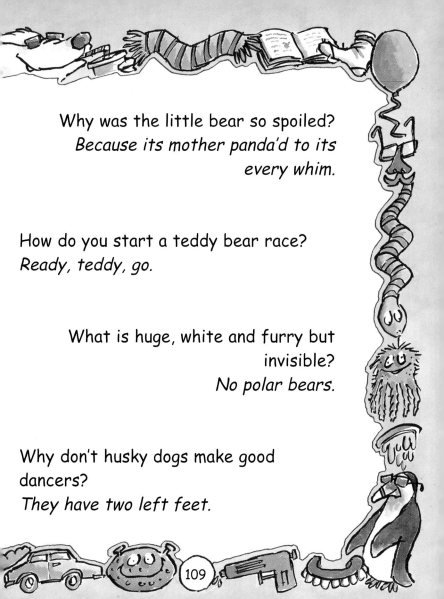

What do Attila the Hun and Winnie the Pooh have in common?
They both have "the" as their middle names.

What do polar bears have for lunch?
Ice burgers.

What do you get if you cross a polar bear and a harp?
A bear-faced lyre.

What do you do if your husky dog eats your pen?
Use a pencil instead.

What's yellow, comes from Peru, and is completely unknown?
Waterloo Bear, Paddington Bear's forgotten cousin.

What do you get if you cross a skunk with a bear?
Winnie the Pooh.

What do you do with two pieces of bread in the desert?
Make a sandwich.

What's a husky dog's favourite hobby?
Collecting fleas.

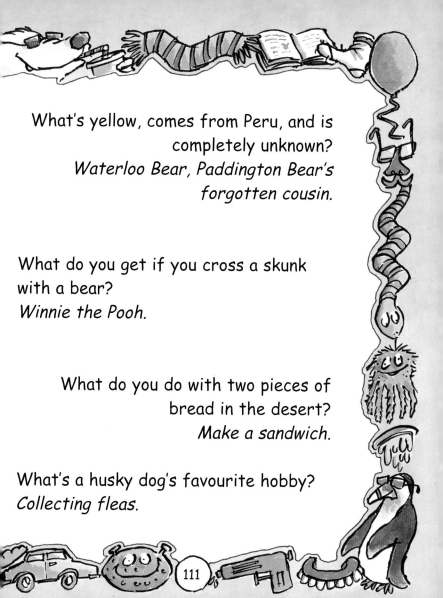

Why did the boat go to the dock?
He was sick.

When does milk make you blink?
When it is already past-eur-ized.

What did the digital watch say to his mum?
Look Mum, no hands.

How did the telephones get married?
In a double ring ceremony.

What do you get if you cross a US President with a shark?
Jaws Washington.

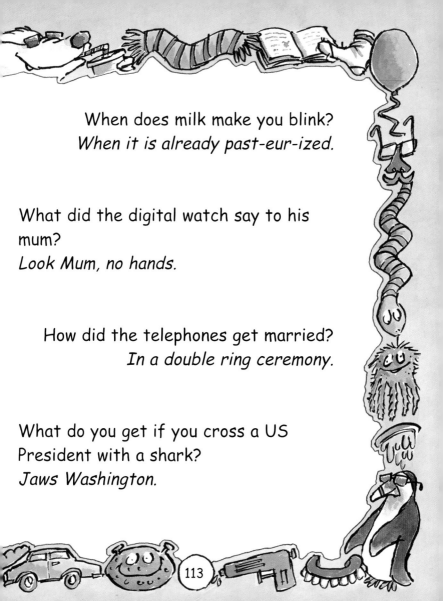

113

Why did the child study in an aeroplane?
He wanted higher education.

Why was the broom late?
It over swept.

Do you know the time?
No, we haven't met yet.

What do you get if you cross a husky dog and a lion?
A terrified postman.

What kind of hair do oceans have?
Wavy.

What runs but never walks?
Water.

How do you make milk shake?
Give it a good scare.

What happened to the husky dog that ate nothing but garlic?
Its bark was much worse than its bite.

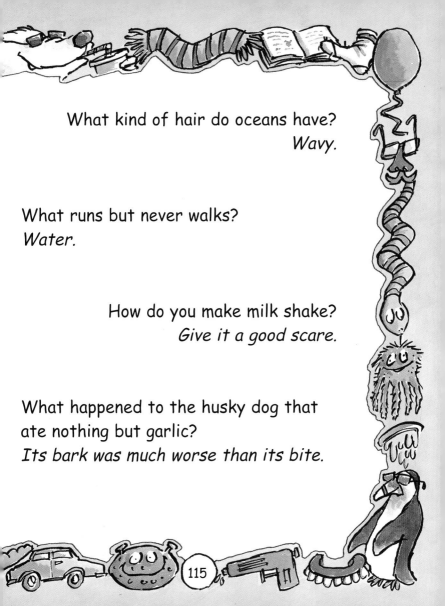

What's red and flies and wobbles at the same time?
A jellycopter.

"Waiter, this soup tastes funny."
"Then why aren't you laughing?"

Why did the clock get sick?
It was run down.

Why do you need a licence for a husky dog and not for a cat?
Cats can't drive.

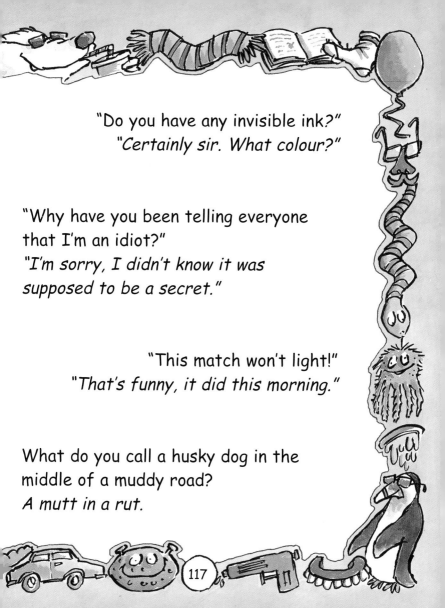

"Do you have any invisible ink?"
"Certainly sir. What colour?"

"Why have you been telling everyone that I'm an idiot?"
"I'm sorry, I didn't know it was supposed to be a secret."

"This match won't light!"
"That's funny, it did this morning."

What do you call a husky dog in the middle of a muddy road?
A mutt in a rut.

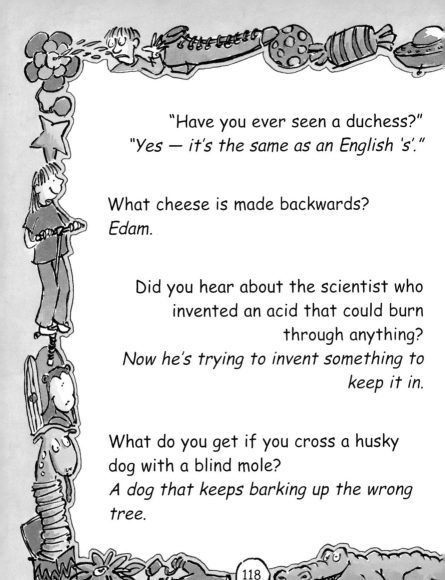

"Have you ever seen a duchess?"
"Yes — it's the same as an English 's'."

What cheese is made backwards?
Edam.

Did you hear about the scientist who
invented an acid that could burn
through anything?
*Now he's trying to invent something to
keep it in.*

What do you get if you cross a husky
dog with a blind mole?
*A dog that keeps barking up the wrong
tree.*

What did the fireman's wife get for
Christmas?
A ladder in her stocking.

What do you get if you cross a Scottish legend and a bad egg?
The Loch Ness Pongster.

What has a bottom at the top?
Your legs.

What is the smelliest city in America?
Phew York.

How do you catch a runaway husky dog?
Hide behind a tree and make a noise like a bone.

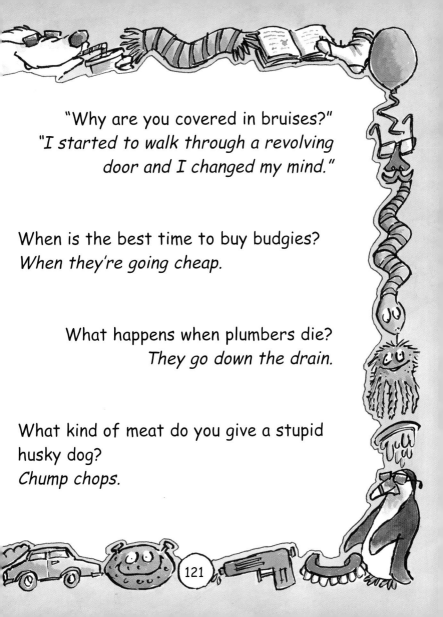

"Why are you covered in bruises?"
*"I started to walk through a revolving
door and I changed my mind."*

When is the best time to buy budgies?
When they're going cheap.

What happens when plumbers die?
They go down the drain.

What kind of meat do you give a stupid
husky dog?
Chump chops.

How do you cure a headache?
Put your head through a window and the pane will just disappear.

Why did the sword-swallower swallow an umbrella?
He wanted to put something away for a rainy day.

What were the gangster's last words?
"Who put that violin in my violin case?"

How many seasons are there in a husky dog's life?
Just one, the moulting season.

What do you call an American drawing?
Yankee doodle.

What do cannibals eat at tea parties?
Chocolate fingers.

What did one virus say to another?
"Stay away! I think I've got penicillin."

What do you call a husky dog with no legs?
It doesn't matter what you call him, he still won't come.

Why did the burglar take a shower?
He wanted to make a clean getaway.

Why do idiots eat biscuits?
Because they're crackers.

What cake wanted to rule the world?
Attila the Bun.

Where does a general keep his armies?
Up his sleevies.

What's wet, black and jumps out of the sea shouting "Knickers!"?
Crude oil.

How did Noah see the animals in the Ark at night?
By flood lighting.

What is hairy and coughs?
A coconut with a cold.

What do you call a foreign body in a chip pan?
An Unidentified Frying Object.

What's wet, black and jumps out of the sea shouting "Underpants!"?
Refined oil.

What did the tie say to the hat?
You go on ahead and I'll hang around.

What did the picture say to the wall?
I've got you covered.

What is the best thing to take into the desert?
A thirst aid kit.

When is a black dog not a black dog?
When it's a greyhound.

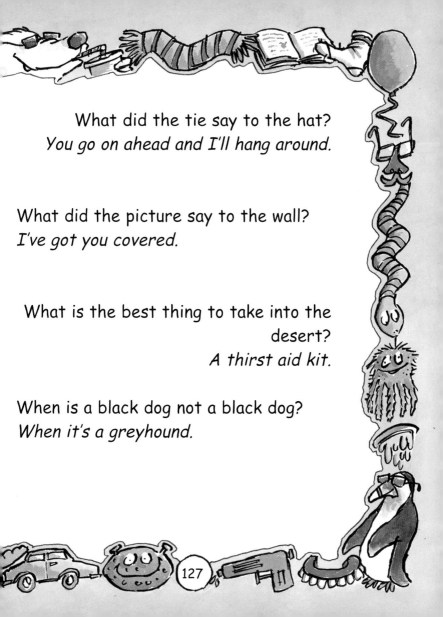

"Who broke the window?"
"It was Bob, he ducked when I threw a stone at him."

Why did the lazy man want a job in a bakery?
So he could loaf around.

"I want a hair cut please."
"Certainly, which one?"

What do you do with a sick kangaroo?
Give it a hoperation.

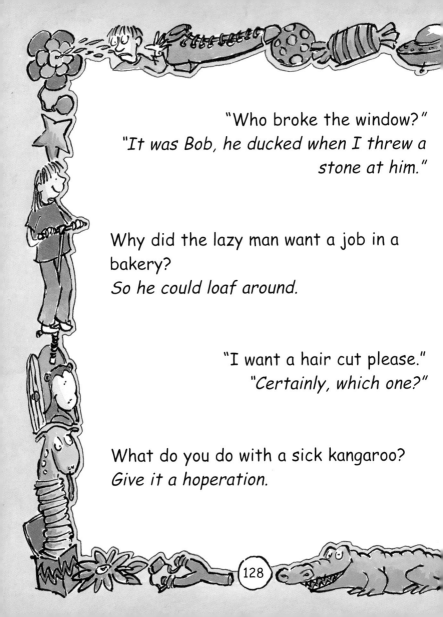

Who was the first underwater spy?
James Pond.

Do you look in the mirror after you've washed your face?
No — you usually look in a towel first.

"You were a long time putting salt in the salt-cellar."
"Well, you can't get much in at a time through those little holes in the top."

Why is it called a litter of puppies?
They mess up the whole house.

Why was the Egyptian girl worried?
Because her daddy was a mummy.

How old is your grandad?
I don't know but we've had him a long time.

"Dad, there is a man at the door collecting for the new swimming pool."
"Give him a glass of water."

What do you get if you cross two young husky dogs with a pair of headphones?
Hush puppies.

"Eat up your spinach, it'll put colour in your cheeks."
"But I don't want green cheeks."

Why did Mickey Mouse take a trip into space?
He wanted to find Pluto.

What happened when the wheel was invented?
It caused a revolution.

Did you hear about the mad scientist who put dynamite in his fridge?
They say it blew his cool.

What do you call young husky dogs who have come in from the snow?
Slush puppies.

"Would you like a duck egg for tea?"
"Only if you quack it for me."

Did you hear about the world's worst
Kamikaze pilot?
He flew forty-two missions.

What city cheats at exams?
Peking.

Why do husky dogs run in circles?
It's hard to run in squares.

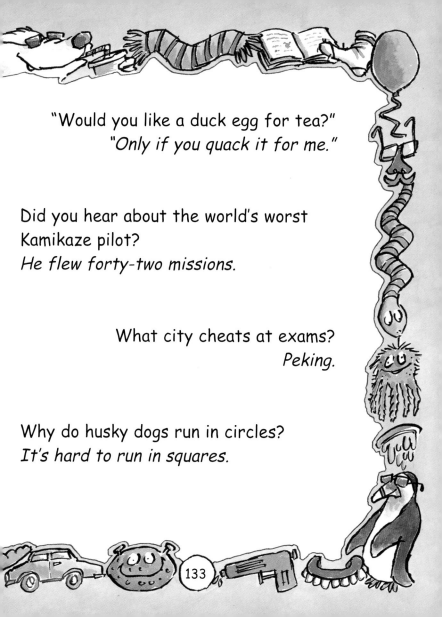

133

What is the fastest thing in water?
A motor pike.

Who is in cowboy films and is always broke?
Skint Eastwood.

Who is the biggest gangster in the sea?
Al Caprawn.

What do you get if you cross a husky dog with a frog?
A dog that can lick you from the other side of the road.

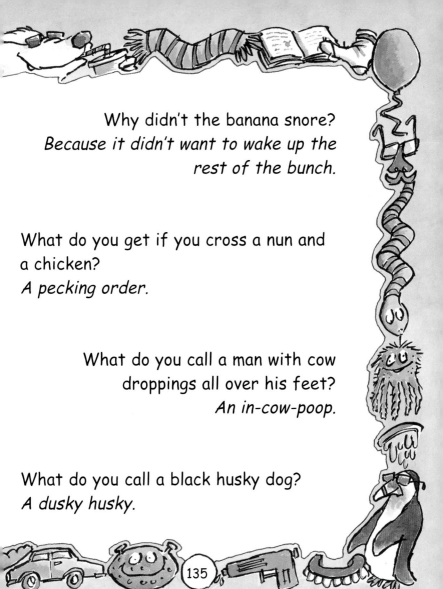

Why didn't the banana snore?
Because it didn't want to wake up the rest of the bunch.

What do you get if you cross a nun and a chicken?
A pecking order.

What do you call a man with cow droppings all over his feet?
An in-cow-poop.

What do you call a black husky dog?
A dusky husky.

Why did the stupid racing driver make ten pit stops during the race?
He was asking for directions.

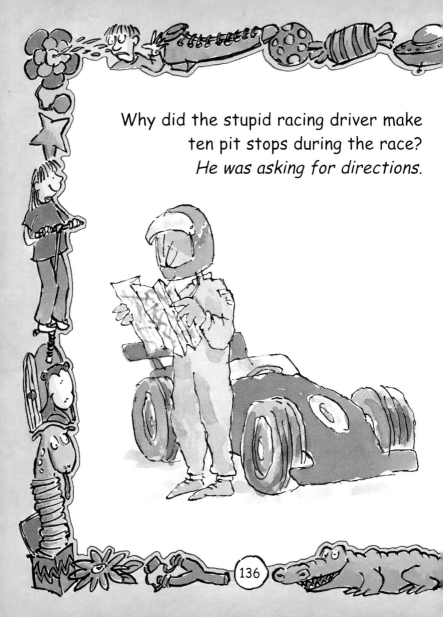

What illness did everyone on the
Starship Enterprise catch?
Chicken Spocks.

What is green and has four legs and
two trunks?
Two seasick tourists.

Why is perfume obedient?
Because it is scent wherever it goes.

When does a husky dog say "Moo!"?
When it is learning a new language.

What soldiers smell of salt and pepper?
Seasoned troops.

Can a match box?
No, but a tin can.

What's the difference between
electricity and lightning?
You don't have to pay for lightning.

What happens to a husky dog that
keeps eating bits off of the table?
He gets splinters in his mouth.

What is a myth?
A female moth.

What is an octopus?
An eight-sided cat.

What did the dog say when he sat on
sandpaper?
"Rufffff."

What do you get if you cross a husky
dog with a skunk?
Rid of the dog.

What do you call a pig that knows karate?
A pork-chop.

Why do mother kangaroos hate rainy days?
Because the kids have to play inside.

What kind of dog can jump higher than a building?
Any dog — buildings can't jump.

What does a young polar bear become after it is four years old?
Five years old.

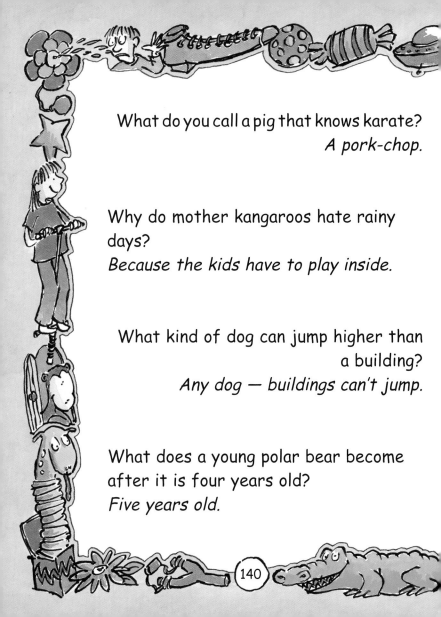

Why did the dog jump into the river?
Because he wanted to catch a catfish.

What does a frog do when its car
breaks down?
Gets it toad off and jump-started.

What is the best year for a kangaroo?
A leap year.

What's brown and sounds like a bell?
Dung.

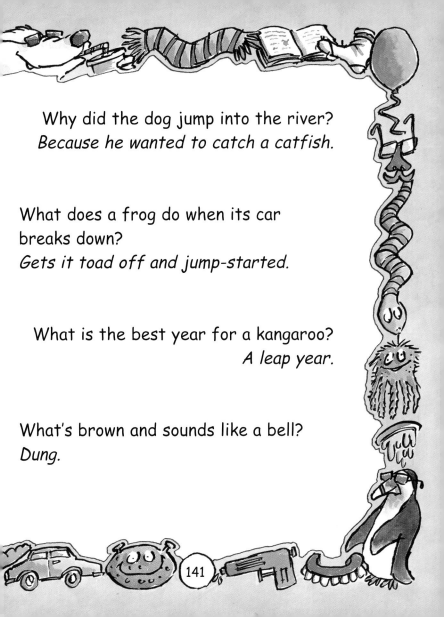

What would happen if pigs could fly?
Bacon would go up.

How do you close an envelope
underwater?
With a seal.

Why do giraffes have long necks?
Because they have smelly feet.

What do you get if you cross a husky
dog with a kangaroo?
*A dog that has somewhere to put its
own lead.*

Where do cats like to go on holiday?
The Canary Islands.

If a dog lost his tail, where would he get another one?
Any re-tail store.

What is a horse's favourite cartoon character?
Whinney the Pooh.

What did the teddy bear say when the monkey offered him dessert?
"No thanks, I'm stuffed."

Which fish can perform operations?
A sturgeon.

What do you get if you cross a stream and a brook?
Wet feet.

Where are whales weighed?
At a whale-weigh station.

How do you spell mousetrap in three letters?
"C-A-T".

Where do little fishes go every morning?
To plaice school.

SUPER COOL

What's worse than raining cats and dogs?
Hailing taxis.

What's the most popular wine at Christmas?
"But Mum, I don't like sprouts . . ."

Why was Santa's little helper depressed?
Because he had low elf-esteem.

What kind of fish is useful in freezing weather?
Skate.

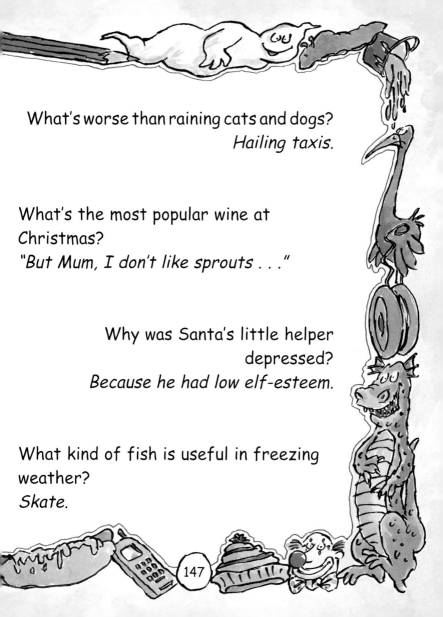

Why does Santa's sled get such good mileage?
Because there are long-distance runners on each side.

What nationality is Father Christmas?
North Polish.

Why did the elf push his bed into the fireplace?
He wanted to sleep like a log.

Why doesn't Santa give his helpers chocolates?
Because too much chocolate is bad for your elf.

What happens once in a minute, twice in a moment, but never in an hour?
The letter "M."

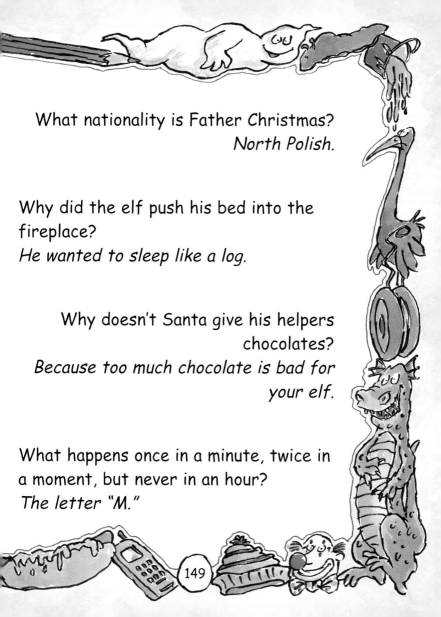

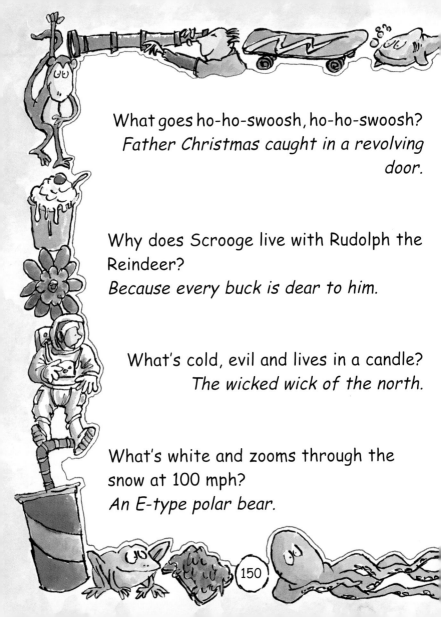

What goes ho-ho-swoosh, ho-ho-swoosh?
Father Christmas caught in a revolving door.

Why does Scrooge live with Rudolph the Reindeer?
Because every buck is dear to him.

What's cold, evil and lives in a candle?
The wicked wick of the north.

What's white and zooms through the snow at 100 mph?
An E-type polar bear.

Have you ever heard of the tenth reindeer, Olive?
She's in the song — "Olive the other reindeer used to laugh and call him names".

What do you call a cat at the beach?
Sandy Claws.

What beats his chest and swings from Christmas cake to Christmas cake?
Tarzipan.

What can you hold without touching it?
A conversation.

What did the arctic fishermen sing
when they got their Christmas dinner?
*"Whalemeat again, don't know where,
don't know when."*

What did the big cracker say to the
little cracker?
"My pop is bigger than yours."

Who is never hungry at Christmas?
The turkey — he's always stuffed.

What happened to the paperboy?
He got blown away.

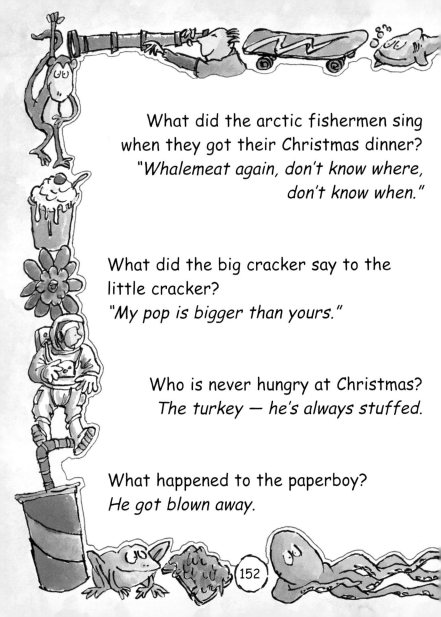

What happens if you eat Christmas decorations?
You get tinsel-itus.

What do vampires put on their turkey at Christmas?
Grave-y.

How do you tell the difference between tinned turkey and tinned custard?
Look at the labels.

What's stupid and yellow?
Thick custard.

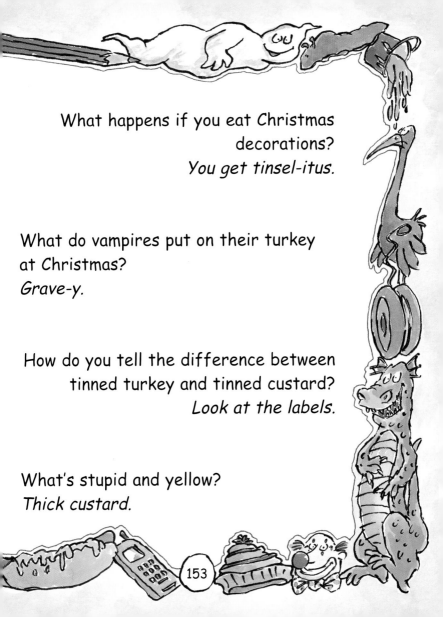

What do reindeer say before telling you a joke?
"This one will sleigh you."

Why do reindeer wear fur coats?
Because they would look silly in plastic anoraks.

How do you make a slow reindeer fast?
Don't feed it.

If a buttercup is yellow, what colour is a hiccup?
Burple.

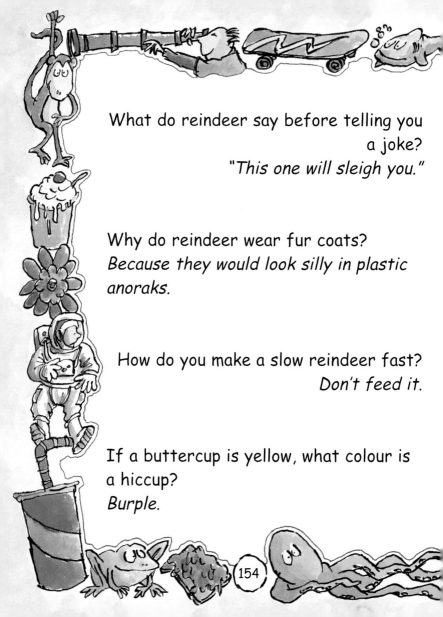

Why did the reindeer wear black boots?
Because his brown ones were all muddy.

How long should a reindeer's legs be?
Just long enough to reach the ground.

Why did the reindeer wear sunglasses at the beach?
Because he didn't want to be recognized.

Which reindeer have the shortest legs?
The smallest ones.

What's the opposite of minimum?
Minidad.

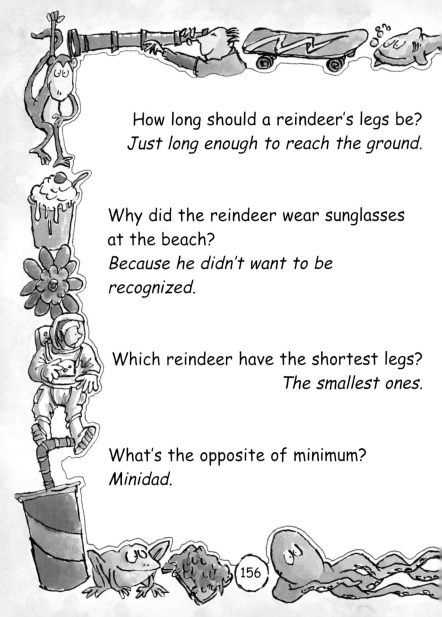

Where do you find reindeer?
It depends on where you leave them.

What animal carries an umbrella?
A rain-deer.

What do reindeer have that no other
animals have?
Baby reindeer.

What do you call an astronaut's watch?
A luna-tic.

How many legs does a reindeer have?
Six. Forelegs at the front and two at the back.

What's the difference between a biscuit and a reindeer?
You can't dunk a reindeer in your tea.

When should you feed reindeer milk to a baby?
When it's a baby reindeer.

What lives in the ocean, is grouchy and hates neighbours?
A hermit crab.

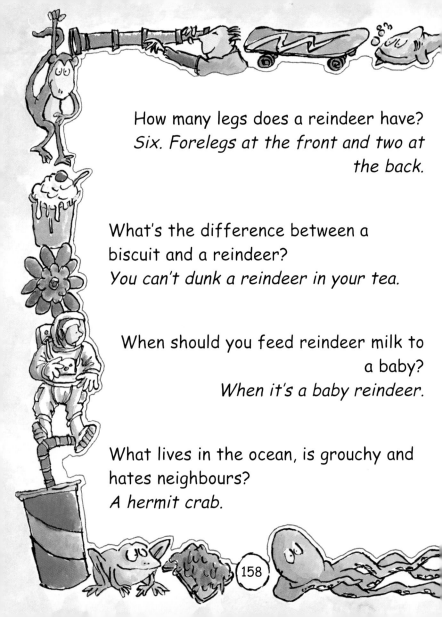

What's black and white and hums?
A dead penguin.

Why do reindeer scratch themselves?
Because they're the only ones who know where they itch.

What did the dog say to the reindeer?
"Woof, woof."

What do you get from a bad-tempered shark?
As far away as possible.

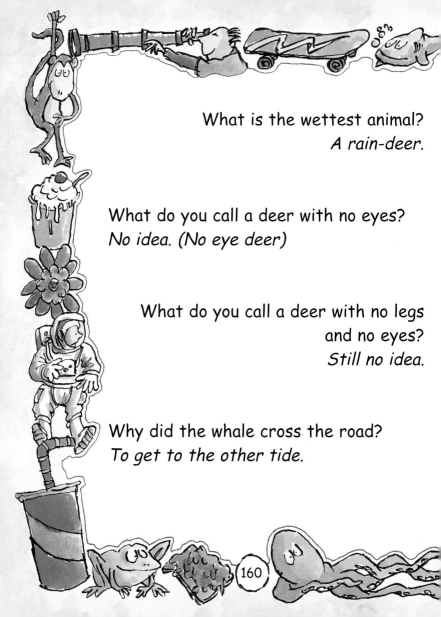

What is the wettest animal?
A rain-deer.

What do you call a deer with no eyes?
No idea. (No eye deer)

What do you call a deer with no legs
and no eyes?
Still no idea.

Why did the whale cross the road?
To get to the other tide.

What did Mrs Santa say when her husband asked her about the weather?
"Looks like rain, dear."

What do you get if you cross Father Christmas with a detective?
Santa Clues.

Father Christmas won a saucepan in a competition.
Now that's what you call pot luck.

What do you call a big fish who makes you an offer you can't refuse?
The Codfather.

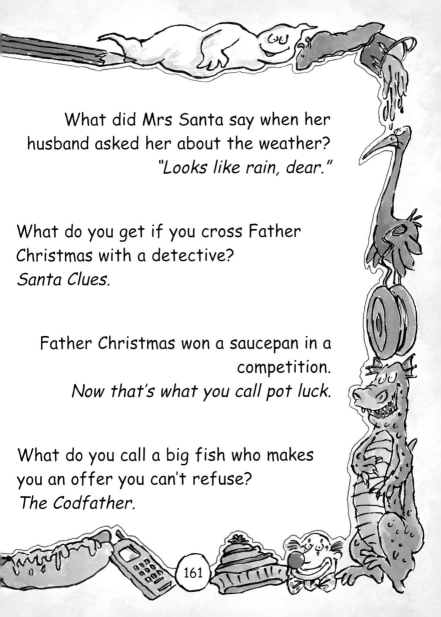

What do you call a man who claps at Christmas?
Santapplause.

Twinkle, twinkle chocolate bar,
Santa drives a rusty car,
Press the starter,
Press the choke,
Off he goes in a cloud of smoke!

What did one angel say to the other?
"Halo there."

What happened to the shark who swallowed a bunch of keys?
He got lockjaw.

Why does Father Christmas like to work in the garden?
Because he likes to hoe, hoe, hoe.

What's Father Christmas called when he takes a rest from delivering presents?
Santa Pause.

Who delivers presents to baby sharks at Christmas?
Santa Jaws.

What do fish sing to each other?
"Salmon-chanted evening".

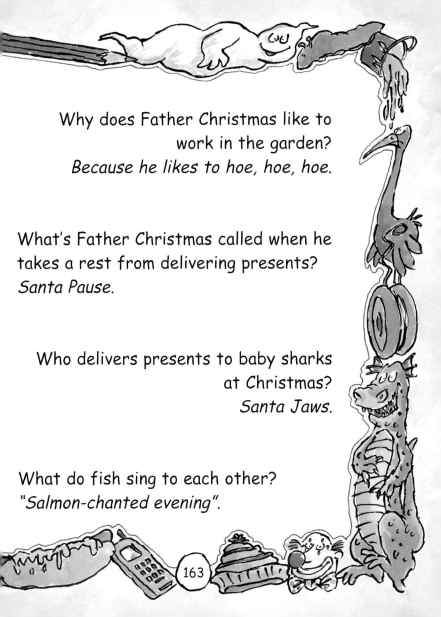

What do Santa's helpers use for cooking?
Elf-raising flour.

What will happen to you at Christmas?
Yule be happy.

What is the best thing to put around a Christmas pudding?
Your mouth.

Why shouldn't you eat reindeer steaks on an empty stomach?
You should eat them on a plate.

How do cats greet each other at Christmas?
"A furry merry Christmas and happy mew year."

What does Dracula write on his Christmas cards?
"Best vicious of the season."

What do angry mice send to each other at Christmas?
Cross mouse cards.

How do we know that Joan of Arc was French?
She was maid in France.

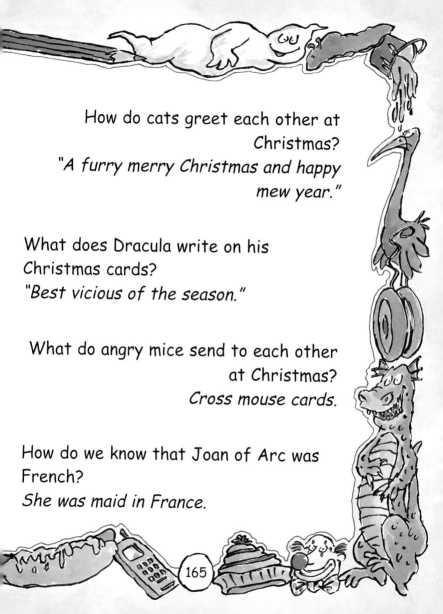

How do sheep greet each other at Christmas?
"A merry Christmas to ewe."

What do snowmen wear on their heads?
Ice caps.

How do snowmen travel around?
By icicle.

What do you get if you cross an abbot with a trout?
Monkfish.

What sort of ball doesn't bounce?
A snowball.

How do you know when there's a
snowman in your bed?
You wake up wet.

What do you get if you cross a snowman
and a shark?
Frost bite.

What is dry on the outside, filled with
water and blows up buildings?
A fish tank.

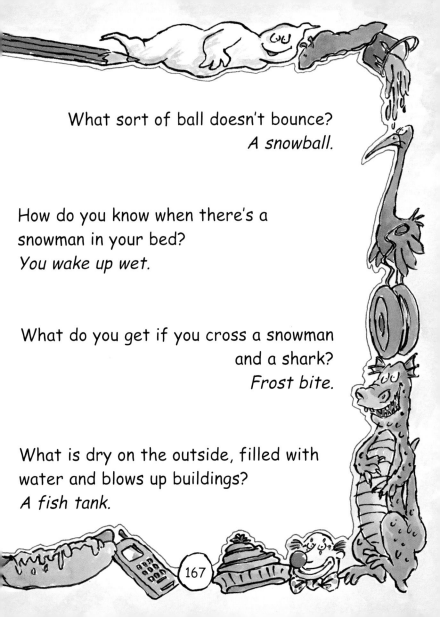

What do you call an arctic cow?
An Eskimoo.

What's the difference between an iceberg and a clothes brush?
One crushes boats and the other brushes coats.

Why did the snow drop?
Because it heard the cro-cus.

Why did the knight run about shouting for a tin opener?
He had a bee in his suit of armour.

What two letters of the alphabet do snowmen prefer?
"I, C."

What do snowmen like with their icebergers?
Chilli sauce.

What stays hot even at the North Pole?
Mustard.

Why were the early days of history called the dark ages?
There were so many knights.

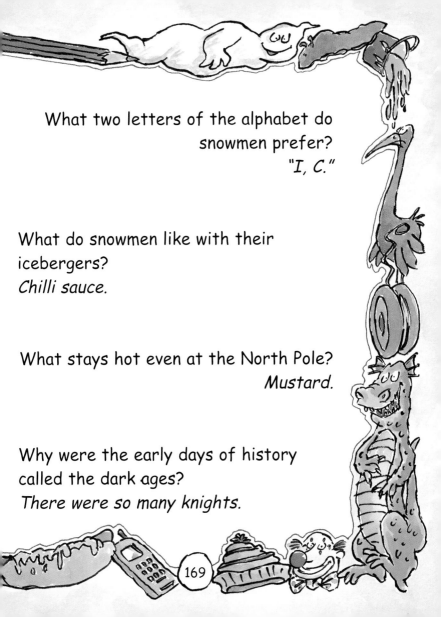

What do you call a penguin in the Sahara desert?
Lost.

What did Adam say on the day before Christmas?
"It's Christmas, Eve."

What do you have in December that you don't have in any other month?
The letter "D".

What's black and white and difficult all over?
An exam paper.

What does Father Christmas suffer
from if he gets stuck in a chimney?
Santa Claustrophobia.

What do you call a letter sent up the
chimney on Christmas Eve?
Black mail.

Who delivers cats' Christmas presents?
Santa Paws.

What was the Tsar of Russia's favourite
fish?
Tsardines.

Why does Father Christmas go down the chimney?
Because it soots him.

How many chimneys does Father Christmas go down?
Stacks.

Who is Santa Claus's wife?
Mary Christmas.

What do you get if you cross a trout with an apartment?
A flat fish.

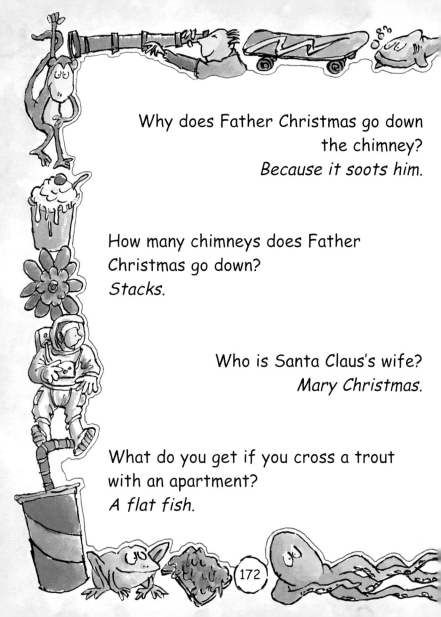

Why is Santa like a bear on Christmas Eve?
Because he's Sooty.

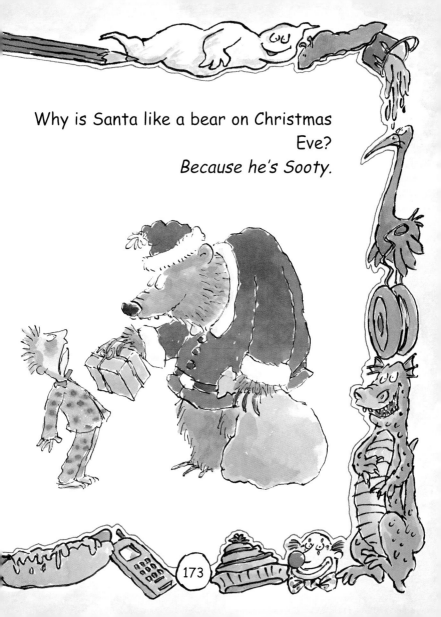

What do monkeys sing at Christmas?
"Jungle bells, jungle bells."

Why are Christmas trees like bad knitters?
They always drop their needles.

What do you call the Ghost of Christmas Past when he's had too much to drink?
A methylated spirit.

How do the fish get to school?
By octobus.

What does the Ghost of Christmas Past
eat for dinner?
Past-a.

What kind of glasses does the Ghost of
Christmas Past wear?
Spook-tacles.

What does the Ghost of Christmas Past
have for breakfast?
Orange boos.

Why do penguins lay eggs?
*Because if they dropped them they
would break on the ice.*

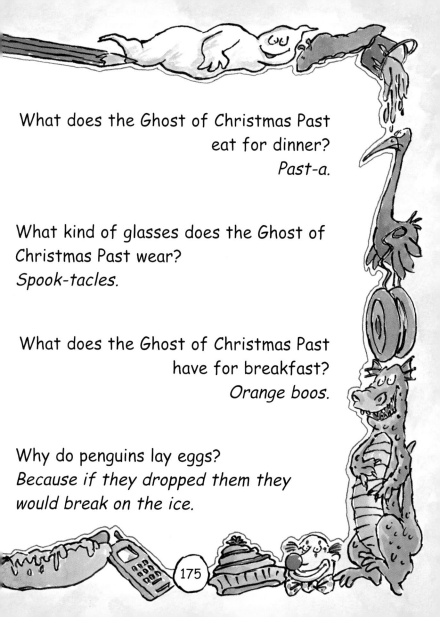

Why does the Ghost of Christmas Past
like tall buildings?
Because of all the scarecases.

What's Christmas called in England?
Yule Britannia.

Why is a burning candle like being thirsty?
*Because a little water ends both of
them.*

What lies on its back a hundred feet up
in the air?
A dead centipede.

Which is fastest, hot or cold?
Hot — it's easy to catch a cold.

What can fall for miles without getting hurt?
Snow.

What happens after a dry spell?
It rains.

Why are sardines the stupidest fish in the sea?
They climb into tins, close the lid and leave the key outside.

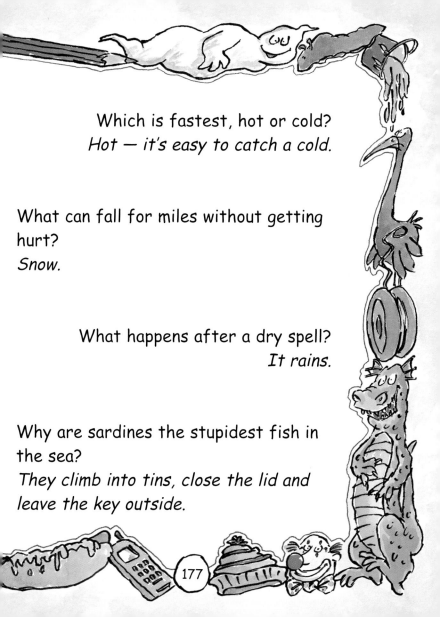

What is the coldest part of the North Pole?
An explorer's nose.

Thirty people were under an umbrella — how many got wet?
None — it wasn't raining.

"Waiter, waiter, there's a fly in my ice cream!"
"I didn't know the winter sports had started so early this year."

What do frogs like to play in the winter?
Ice hoppy.

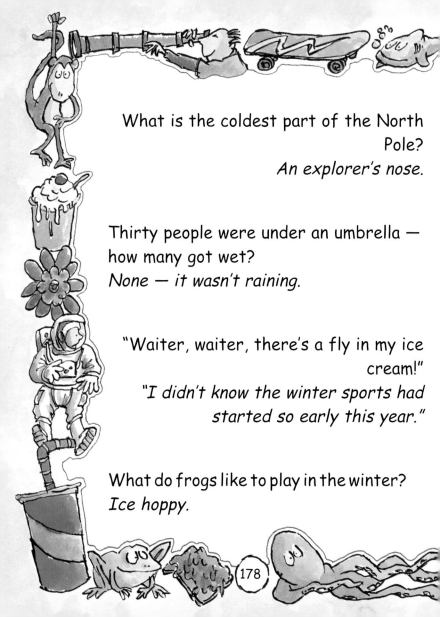

If two's company and three's a crowd, what is four and five?
Nine.

What do you get if you cross an apple with a Christmas tree?
A pineapple.

What do you give a train driver for Christmas?
Platform shoes.

What's the best way to prevent infection from a polar bear bite?
Don't bite any polar bears.

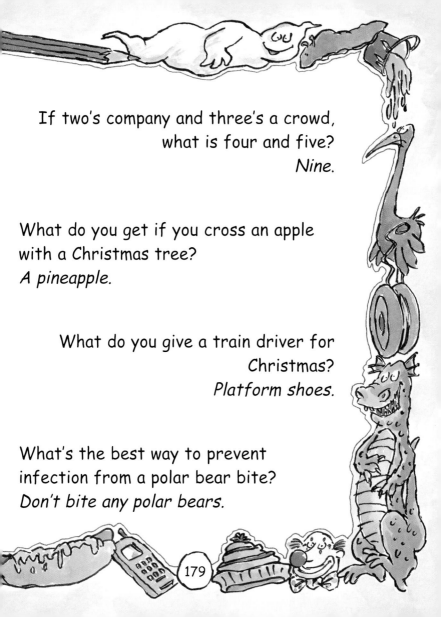

What did the big candle say to the little candle?
"I'm going out tonight."

What's round and bad-tempered?
A vicious circle.

Why did the doughnut shop close?
The owner was tired of the hole business.

What's black and white, lives in the Antarctic and is highly dangerous?
A penguin with a machine gun.

How long does it take to burn a candle down?
About a wick.

What do you call a dog that gets mail?
A golden receiver.

What did the duck say to the comedian after the show?
"You really quacked me up."

Why are fish boots the warmest ones to wear?
They have electric eels.

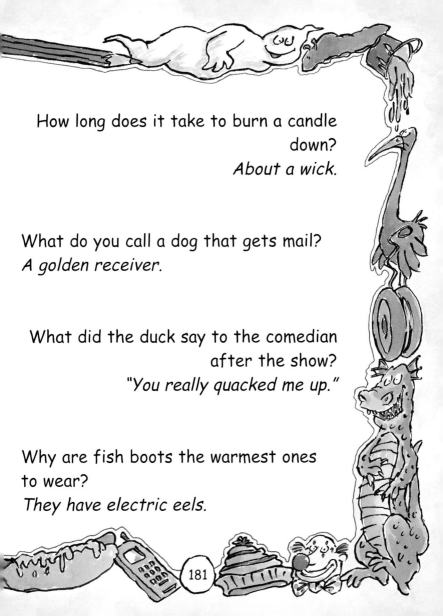

How much do chickens pay for their trainers?
A poultry amount.

Why are some fish at the bottom of the ocean?
Because they dropped out of their school.

Why did the farmer take hay to bed?
He wanted to feed his nightmares.

What is a dog's favourite snack?
Pupcorn.

What happens when sharks take their clothes off?
They go sharkers.

Why did the cat run from the tree?
It barked.

Ten cats were on a boat, one jumped
off, how many were left?
None, they were all copycats.

What's the best thing to put in a pie?
Your teeth.

What's yellow and goes putt, putt, putt?
An outboard banana.

What is black and shiny, lives in trees
and is very dangerous?
A crow with a machine gun.

Where do cows dance?
At the meatball.

What do astronauts like to eat?
Mission chips.

Why do white sheep eat more than
black ones?
There are more of them.

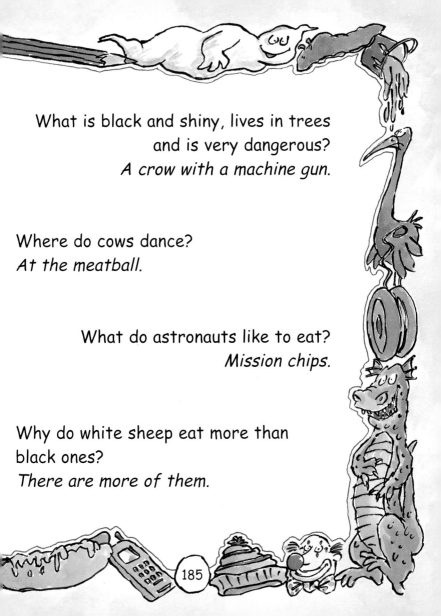

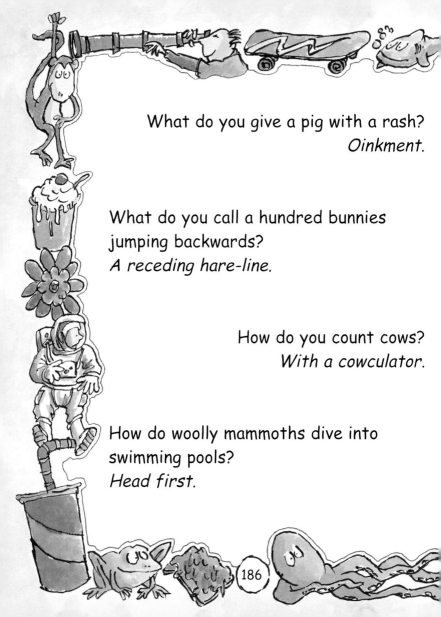

What do you give a pig with a rash?
Oinkment.

What do you call a hundred bunnies
jumping backwards?
A receding hare-line.

How do you count cows?
With a cowculator.

How do woolly mammoths dive into
swimming pools?
Head first.

What do frogs order in restaurants?
French flies.

What day of the week do fish hate?
Fry-day.

Where does a fish keep his money?
In a riverbank.

What is everybody in the world doing at the same time?
Growing older.

What's black and white and can't turn around in a corridor?
A nun with a plank of wood.

Why does a hummingbird hum?
It doesn't know the words.

Did you put the cat out?
I didn't know it was on fire.

What kind of bird is religious?
A bird of prey.

What do you call a rabbit that is owned
by a beetle?
A Bug's Bunny.

What's green and loud?
A froghorn.

What travels at a hundred miles per
hour underground?
A mole on a motorcycle.

How do you know if you've been made
upside-down?
Your nose runs and your feet smell.

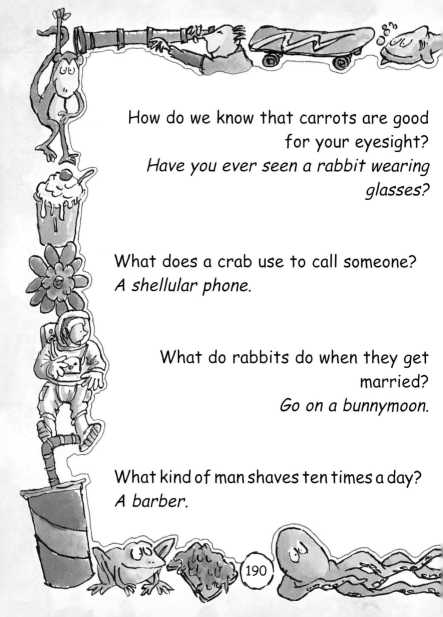

How do we know that carrots are good for your eyesight?
Have you ever seen a rabbit wearing glasses?

What does a crab use to call someone?
A shellular phone.

What do rabbits do when they get married?
Go on a bunnymoon.

What kind of man shaves ten times a day?
A barber.

What kind of key opens a banana?
A monkey.

What do you call a cow with only two legs?
Lean beef.

What has one horn and gives milk?
A milk truck.

Why were the woolly mammoths the last to leave Noah's ark?
They had to pack their trunks.